# AQUINAS AND KANT

*Man is the measure of all things.*
                                    —Protagoras


*God ought to be to us the measure of all things, and not man, as men commonly say : the words are far more true of Him.*
                                    —Plato

# AQUINAS AND KANT

*The Foundations of the Modern Sciences*

by

GAVIN ARDLEY

LONGMANS, GREEN AND CO
LONDON · NEW YORK · TORONTO

LONGMANS, GREEN AND CO LTD
6 & 7 CLIFFORD STREET LONDON W I
ALSO AT MELBOURNE AND CAPE TOWN
LONGMANS, GREEN AND CO INC
55 FIFTH AVENUE NEW YORK 3
LONGMANS, GREEN AND CO
215 VICTORIA STREET TORONTO I
ORIENT LONGMANS LTD
BOMBAY CALCUTTA MADRAS

*First Published 1950*

PRINTED IN GREAT BRITAIN BY
JOHN BELLOWS LIMITED, GLOUCESTER

# PREFACE

THERE are some possessions, observes St. Augustine, which are not diminished by being shared, and which, on the contrary, are not fully possessed unless they are shared. Such a possession is the *philosophia perennis*, whose inexhaustible treasury grows richer the more it is drawn upon.

Some have expounded the principles of this human wisdom; some, proceeding further, by means of the steady light thus provided, have reached a deeper understanding of the world. In the work which follows, the light is directed to the sciences of the natural order, sciences which, though profane, yet have a not dishonourable place in the hierarchy of the temporal dispensation in which we find ourselves.

'A man of understanding shall attain unto wise counsels,' says Solomon. In such a work as this, much judicious counsel must be sought out; those to whom I am more immediately indebted are: Vernon Rice, who placed at my disposal his encyclopaedic knowledge of all things Scholastic, Joyce Ardley, who brought much intelligent and helpful criticism, and John Willis, who read the proofs with a keen and watchful eye.

*July* 1949                                                    G.A.

# ACKNOWLEDGMENTS

Acknowledgments are due to the following for permission to include copyright material :—

Messrs. Geoffrey Bles Ltd., for passages from *The Degrees of Knowledge* by J. Maritain ; Messrs. Chatto & Windus, and Messrs. Harper & Brothers, New York, for a passage from *Time Must Have a Stop* by Aldous Huxley ; The Clarendon Press for passages from *An Autobiography* by R. G. Collingwood ; Messrs. Routledge & Kegan Paul Ltd., for passages from *Scientific Method* by A. D. Ritchie, and from *Tractatus Logico-Philosophicus* by L. Wittgenstein ; Messrs. Charles Scribner's Sons, New York, for passages from *Mind and the World Order* by C. I. Lewis ; Messrs. Sheed & Ward Ltd., for passages from *Gilbert Keith Chesterton* by Maisie Ward ; Professor Norman Kemp Smith for passages from his translation of Kant's *Critique of Pure Reason* ; Messrs. Taylor & Francis Ltd., for passages from 'Aristotle, Newton, Einstein,' by Professor E. P. Whittaker, in *The Philosophical Magazine, XXXIV.*

'The Unbeliever' by E. V. Knox is reproduced by permission of the Proprietors of *Punch*; the passage from 'The Windhover' from the *Collected Poems of Gerard Manley Hopkins* is reproduced by permission of the poet's family and the Oxford University Press.

# CONTENTS

## PART I

# INTRODUCTION

*The straightening of the crooked rests on the knowledge of the straight, and the exercise of criticism requires a canon.*

F. H. BRADLEY

*For since it is in the very nature of man to follow the guide of reason in his actions, if his intellect sins at all his will soon follows ; and thus it happens that looseness of intellectual opinion influences human actions and perverts them.   Whereas, on the other hand, if men be of sound mind and take their stand on true and solid principles, there will result a vast amount of benefits for the public and private good.*

LEO XIII

*The metaphysical structure of reality itself does not change.   ' Perennis philosophia ' is not an honorary title for any particular form of philosophical thinking, but a necessary designation for philosophy itself, almost a tautology.   That which is philosophical is also perennial in its own right. . . .*
*Metaphysics remains the knowledge of the first principle, and of all the rest in the light of that principle.   Thus grounded on existence, as on the most universal object of intellect, it is its permanent duty to order and to regulate an ever wider area of scientific knowledge, and to judge ever more complex problems of human conduct ;  it is its never-ended task to keep the old sciences in their natural limits, to assign their places, and their limits, to new sciences ;  last, not least, to keep all human activities, however changing their circumstances, under the sway of the same reason by which alone man remains the judge of his own works, and, after God, the master of his own destiny.*

ETIENNE GILSON

# CHAPTER I

# THE TASK OF PHILOSOPHY

AS so ably enunciated by Gilson, it is the task of those who profess the *philosophia perennis* to assign the places and demarcate the limits of the sciences, old and new. For the last half century, since the Leonine revival in Scholastic philosophy, much work has been done in refurbishing the apparatus of the *philosophia perennis* for this task of criticism. Several centuries of lee-way had to be made up, for relatively little critical work had been done by Scholastic philosophers since the close of the Middle Ages.

In recent years much attention has been devoted by the Scholastics to the many intellectual and scientific movements which have held the stage of history from the 17th century until the present day. Many of these movements have been critically examined, and judgments have been passed on them, as well as may be, in the light of the Scholastic principles.

It should be made clear that this criticism, if truly performed, is not arrogant, or carping, or destructive. It is, on the contrary, judicial. The effect of such an enquiry can only be salutary for all parties concerned. It will help to bring sanity into the babel of tongues which now assails us on every hand. It will help to give back to us the serene perspective which 'the multitude's multitudinous formulae' tend to destroy.

In the course of these critical enquiries some difficult problems have been brought to light, problems which are crying aloud for solution. In the certitude of our established principles we may be confident that all problems are inherently soluble. Our task is the exact delineation of the solutions.

In the field of moral philosophy a major problem has arisen. This is the question of the extent of moral responsibility in abnormal mental and physical states, as seen in the light of modern medicine, psychology, and psychiatry. Much work has yet to be done in this field before final conclusions can be reached. Similarly the growth of anthropology as a science has raised difficult questions about the origin and relativity of moral standards: questions which must be answered before this field of knowledge can be properly incorporated into Scholastic studies.

Perhaps the greatest problem for the Scholastic critic is presented by the physical science of the post-Renaissance period. The theories on the subject put forward by modern Scholastic philosophers are still halting. It is one of the major tasks of the present work to examine this whole matter with care, and to lay down the principles of a general solution.

Another, and, as will appear, closely allied problem, is that of what we might term 'modern logic.' This is a topic which is being advanced with more and more insistence in our day, and it requires careful consideration. The solution offered here will, we hope, throw light on many other matters which are at present obscure.

In a similar way we will enquire into the nature and growth of the new 'social sciences,' and examine their relations to the older rational sciences occupying corresponding fields.

Let us first cast a backward glance to an earlier period when philosophers were likewise confronted with the task of sifting and assimilating a mass of new doctrines.

In the 13th century the works of Aristotle, newly introduced into Western Europe, were convulsing the learned world. The Christian Doctors were confronted with a comprehensive pre-Christian system of thought of great scope and penetration, which had recourse to human reason only, and not to revelation. Many articles of the Aristotelean philosophy were, at least *prima facie*, at variance with the theology of the Christian Fathers and with the Faith itself. Because of this, the study of Aristotle was widely condemned, and many proponents of the new philosophy were persecuted and even proscribed.

It seemed that Christendom was heading for a major schism between the theologians and the philosophers. A precisely similar schism on the same question, a few centuries earlier, had rent Islam in twain. But fortunately in Christendom wiser counsels prevailed, and a synthesis which would do justice to both parties was looked for.[1]

In the assurance that Truth cannot be self-contradictory, it was necessary to seek out a harmony between the rational principles of Aristotle and the Christian revelation. This was the task undertaken by St. Thomas Aquinas. The Thomist harmony of faith and reason solved the problem confronting the 13th century.

Now, in the 20th century, we have a multitude of new problems, and new harmonies to be sought. Our task today is to pick up the threads where they were left by St. Thomas, and carry on. For the *philosophia perennis* is not a closed and static system. It is something which should be ever developing like the great oak tree growing from the acorn.

The Thomist philosophy has elicited principles of Truth, which, as such, are eternal and unchanging. But within the bounds of these principles indefinite development may take place. The principles provide us with the means to judge of new developments, and to see them in their proper perspective. Hence the task of the Scholastic philosopher is never ending, for new problems are ever coming forward to be solved.

The present work is intended as a contribution to this labour of love. It has been entitled *Aquinas and Kant* for this reason : Aquinas represents the metaphysician of the *philosophia perennis*. Kant on the other hand, as we understand him, in his basic contentions gets to the heart of the characteristic non-metaphysical pre-occupations of the modern world. These pre-occupations seem, *prima facie*, to be alien to the

---

[1] On this subject in general see Christopher Dawson: *Religion and Medieval Science*, an essay contained in his *Medieval Religion* (London, 1934). Also his *The Making of Europe* (London, 1932), p. 122 ff. Much historical research has been done in recent years on the origins of Christian Aristoteleanism. A work which throws considerable light on this vital subject is *Aristote en Occident* by Fernand van Steenberghen (Louvain, 1946).

*philosophia perennis.* Consequently the juxtaposition of Aquinas and Kant throws the medieval-modern conflict into high relief. It is the purpose of this work to moderate the conflict, and to show that what is *basic* to Kant is not really alien to Aquinas, but that they are, on the contrary, complementary.

In this way we will clear up metaphysical difficulties about modern physics, and at the same time difficulties about ' modern logic ' and related pursuits.

Aquinas and Kant may seem at first sight to be strange bedfellows ; so did the Fathers and Aristotle some seven centuries ago. The earlier conflict was eventually resolved ; so can be the later.

This task having been accomplished, we have freed ourselves from an irksome entanglement which restrains us in the depths of that cave of which Plato tells us. The shackles having been cast off, we are free to reach up to the distant mouth and ultimately behold the brightness of the sun. It is a liberation which Thomas Carlyle sought after so earnestly :

What in such a time as ours it requires a Prophet or Poet to teach us, namely, the stripping-off of those poor undevout wrappages, nomenclatures and scientific hearsays,—this, the ancient earnest soul, as yet unencumbered with these things, did for itself. The world, which is now divine only to the gifted, was then divine to whosoever would turn his eye upon it. He stood bare before it face to face.[1]

Gerard Manley Hopkins, as he watched the Windhover, was just such a man after Carlyle's own heart :

> *Brute beauty and valour and act, oh, air, pride, plume, here*
> *Buckle ! AND the fire that breaks from thee then, a billion*
> *Times told lovelier, more dangerous, O my chevalier !*
> *No wonder of it : shéer plód makes plough down sillion*
> *Shine, and blue-bleak embers, ah my dear,*
> *Fall, gall themselves, and gash gold–vermilion.*

Here, we may hope, we have done something to resolve the puzzlement involved in the stripping-off of those poor undevout wrappages, in gashing the blue-bleak embers.

---

[1] *Heroes and Hero Worship*, Lecture I.

# CHAPTER II

# PHYSIS AND NOMOS

SOCRATES : *But would you say, Hermogenes, that the things differ as the names differ ? and are they relative to individuals, as Protagoras tells us ? For he says that man is the measure of all things, and that things are to me as they appear to me, and that they are to you as they appear to you. Do you agree with him, or would you say that things have a permanent essence of their own ?*

HERMOGENES : *There have been times, Socrates, when I have been driven in my perplexity to take refuge with Protagoras ; not that I agree with him at all. . . .*

SOCRATES : *But . . . if things are not relative to individuals, and all things do not equally belong to all at the same moment and always, they must be supposed to have their own proper and permanent essence : they are not in relation to us, or influenced by us, fluctuating according to our fancy, but they are independent, and maintain to their own essence the relation prescribed by nature.*

HERMOGENES : *I think, Socrates, that you have said the truth.*

PLATO : *Cratylus* 385–6

## The Two Orders

AS a preliminary to their discussions philosophers frequently analyse the world into parts which they then proceed to examine. As an instance let us take Kant's statement in the *Critique of Pure Reason*. He writes[1] :

Transcendental analytic consists in the dissection of all our *a priori* knowledge into the elements that pure understanding by itself yields.

Let us consider what is involved in this process of analysis or dissection. In 'dissection' it is instructive to compare the practices of, say, the anatomist and the butcher. When an

[1] *Critique of Pure Reason*, B 89.

anatomist dissects a rabbit or a sheep he traces out the real structure of the animal. He lays bare the veins, the nerves, the muscles, the organs, and so on. He reveals the actual structure which is there before him waiting to be made manifest. But when the butcher chops up the animal, he is not particularly concerned with the real structure; he wants to cut up the carcase into joints suitable for domestic purposes. In his activities the butcher ruthlessly cleaves across the real structure laid bare so patiently by the anatomist. The anatomist *finds* his structure, the butcher *makes* his. The one pursuit is of the real, that of which, we may say, God is the fashioner or creator. In the other case man himself is the fashioner or creator, or rather the re-creator. Man becomes, in a minor way, his own god. To this extent Protagoras was right when he said ' Man is the measure of all things.' It is certainly true that man is the measure of *some* things, even though not of *all*.

The anatomist proceeds by inspection, by recognition of what is *objectively* there, using the senses with which he has been endowed. The activity of the butcher on the other hand is directed *subjectively*, and is literally, as well as metaphorically, the procedure of the Procrustean bed.[1]

We can compare this contrast with the old contrast which agitated the Greek world in the 5th and 4th centuries B.C. : that between *physis* and *nomos*. The Greeks were usually at pains to separate and distinguish clearly what was *physis* from what was *nomos*.

The word *physis* can perhaps best be translated by the English word *nature*. The *physis* of things for the Greek philosopher meant the real nature of things, the underlying reality behind the appearances, the thread so to speak which persisted through change. The *physis* then is the unchanging reality.

The antithesis to this is *nomos* or *law*. *Nomos* is that which exists not by nature, but by artifice, convention, custom, or usage. It is man-made, and not part of the everlasting order of the world.

[1] See Ch. III.

## Plato and the Sophists

The contrast of nature and law was a favourite theme of the Sophists. They, or many of them, maintained that codes of laws and set customs and morality were merely man-made and conventional, and were not embedded in the nature of things at all. This tended to discredit customary morality and law, since if they are not of the nature of things then what sanction can they have? It was this situation which confronted Socrates and Plato, who endeavoured to refute the Sophists and establish that morality was not merely *nomos*, but was of the *physis*, and hence a part of the real world, and immutable, and binding on all.

As an example, let us consider the case of the sophist Protagoras. Protagoras seems to express the doctrine that all things are *nomos*, in his famous dictum 'Man is the measure of all things.' Precisely what Protagoras meant by this has since been the subject of much controversy. It may have been a doctrine of extreme individualism : that every man is as wise as any other. This interpretation is suggested and adversely criticised by Plato in the *Theaetetus*.[1] But it seems more likely that Protagoras was pointing out how conventional things are, and how right it is that this should be so. The common opinion of mankind in a normal state thus becomes the ultimate criterion. Law and morality are, as it were, social constructions, and it is our wisdom to abide by these conventions. Hence with the doctrine of Protagoras we have gone full circle, for now the sophist doctrine is no longer revolutionary but extremely conservative. In this respect Protagoras affords a good example of a seeming paradox which is common throughout history. This is, that if you abandon an objective reality you fly into the arms of a rigid convention, because there is then nothing more to appeal to beyond convention.

The common sense of man then is the legislator according to Protagoras. It will be seen that if this interpretation of Protagoras' dictum be correct, and if he insisted literally on *all* things, then for Protagoras the antithesis of *physis* and

[1] *Theaetetus,* 161B.

*nomos* has vanished because of the removal altogether of the *physis*.

Speaking in general, the *physis* is that which is ordained by God; the *nomos* is that which is ordained by man. Plato takes up this theme in his last work, *The Laws*. Plato, as the end draws near, puts less trust than ever in man, and more in the hand of God. He writes :

God ought to be to us the measure of all things, and not man, as men commonly say (Protagoras) : the words are far more true of Him. And he who would be dear to God must, as far as is possible, be like Him and such as He is.[1]

Protagoras, with his doctrine that language, morals, customs, laws, have no divine sanction, but are man-made, is the antithesis to Plato, and provides the Magna Carta of 'humanism.' In fact, the whole 'humanist' movement may be said to rest on Protagoras. It shares his strength and his weakness. 'The philosophy of man began only with Protagoras ' says a contemporary author, Popper.[2] He regards Protagoras as the theorist of what he calls the 'Open Society' while Plato is the theorist of the 'Closed Society.' The Open Society is one, so Popper claims, which sets free the critical powers of man, while the Closed Society is an arrested society in which unity is maintained by an unquestioning and irrational appeal to supernatural forces and tribal taboos.

However, as we have just pointed out, the *ultimate* result of a doctrine like that of Protagoras, that everything is *nomos*, far from being a liberation, is a paralysis of the worst kind. For if everything is convention then we cannot make the appeal to what 'really is the case' which is the basis of all rational social change. This is the fallacy of any merely humanitarian scheme.

Only when we can have recourse to a *physis*, something to appeal to beyond convention, can society be really alive and growing. 'Only the permanent can change' is a verbal paradox, but nevertheless profoundly true.

[1] *Laws*, 716.
[2] Popper, K. : *The Open Society and its Enemies* (London, 1945), *v.* 1, p. 166.

*The Two Orders and Law*

A further illustration of *physis* and *nomos* may be taken from the contrast of juridical natural law with human positive law. In the classical exposition by St. Thomas Aquinas it is laid down that:

There is an eternal law, namely the reason existing in the mind of God, by which the whole universe is governed. And: The rational creature has itself a share in the eternal reason and derives from this its natural inclination towards its proper action and end ; and this manner of sharing in the eternal law, which is peculiar to the rational creature, is called the natural law.[1]

It is clear that this natural law partakes of what the Greek philosophers called the *physis* of things.

But as well as the eternal and natural law there exists a human positive law. This is necessary because man's capacity for sharing in the divine reason was weakened by the Fall, and now he can only participate according to the measure of his own imperfect nature.

In the sphere of practical reason man participates by nature in the natural law to the extent of certain universal principles, but not to the extent of specific rules for particular actions, although these also are contained in the eternal law. Hence it is necessary to proceed by human reasoning beyond the first principles to legal enactment of certain particular rules.

Thus we have two systems of law : the natural law and the human or positive law. And, of course, corresponding to these two systems of law, are two systems of rights : natural rights and positive civil rights.

Natural rights, like natural law, are inalienable, and are the possession of every man quite independently of the State. They partake of the *physis*. They are God-given. On the other hand the positive law, and the rights arising from it, are subject to the State and depend for their existence on recognition by the State. They are plainly of the order of *nomos* in the Greek terminology. They are man-made, conventional, customary. Man is the legislator; the positive rights obey

[1] *Summa Theologica*, Prima Secundae, Question xci : ' Of the various kinds of law.'

Protagoras' dictum that 'man is the measure.' But the
important point is that man is not the measure of *all* things.
The area in which man is the measure is limited by the natural
law. The addition of *all* things was the fatal mistake made by
Protagoras. It meant swallowing up the *physis* in the *nomos*.
*The truth is that there is both 'physis' and 'nomos.' In a well-
governed state these two exist together in harmony.* There will be no
collision between these two systems of rights and laws since
in the good state human law is made always with reference to
natural law and is always conformable to it. The natural
law forms, as it were, a framework inside which human law
enjoys autonomy.

If any actual law is unjust, i.e. is contrary to natural law,
we have a basis of protest against it. The recognition of these
principles gives a man a soul to call his own, it makes room for
the reformer, it leaves us knowing that after all the individual
person is *not* submerged in society.

Our conclusion then is that St. Thomas leaves room for a
*moderate* Protagoras.

*Philosophical Momentum*

The immoderation of Protagoras himself is an example of
an all too common tendency in philosophy. A philosopher
takes hold of a true principle, and then rides it to death. He
pushes it far beyond its valid sphere of application. This is
always the pitfall for the philosopher broaching a new subject.
It is only when philosophical movements are considerably
matured that a reasonable balance is achieved. Great
philosophical syntheses are reached as a rule long after the
turbulent births of the constituent philosophies. The medieval
synthesis of St. Thomas was achieved some thousand years
or more after the great days of the ancient philosophies. It
is from such a serene perspective that we must look, not for
mere novelty, but for truth.

Why was Protagoras' original doctrine so immoderate?
The historical reasons are not far to seek. The Greek world
was emerging from something like a tribal society to what we

may conveniently call an 'open' society. A tribal society is ruled by rigid customs, obeyed in detail practically without question. The customs tend to be regarded as immutable and embedded in the nature of things. On the break-up of this primal unity and the transition to a diverse, humanitarian, 'open', society, as so often happens, the philosophers in the forefront of the movement pushed the new ideas to absurd lengths. Protagoras no doubt saw that much which had once been regarded as in the nature of things was really only customary and man-made. The legislation of a Lycurgus or a Solon is scarcely of divine origin. This meant that not everything is of the *physis*. Some is merely *nomos*. But Protagoras abandoned moderation and went to the other extreme and tried to make *everything* of the *nomos*. Man is certainly the measure of *some* things, but he is equally certainly not the measure of *all* things. This was Protagoras' mistake. In general, every exaggeration is countered by a contrary exaggeration, and in this way history and philosophy advance dialectically to greater heights. It is in final syntheses that we look for truth.

*Conclusions*

We have now drawn the general distinction of *physis* and *nomos* and given some examples to illustrate the two. These constitute what we may call two orders : the real or natural, on the one hand, and the conventional or artificial, on the other ; the God-made and the man-made ; the objective and, in a sense, the subjective, or better the anthropocentric or sociocentric.

Another convenient term we may employ for the second order is '*categorial*'[1] because the activity of man as the measure usually involves dividing the world and allotting it into some sort of conventional classes or categories. Thus we

---

[1] This is a term used by e.g. Professor Broad (see *The Mind and its Place in Nature* (London, 1925), p. 265). It has obvious Kantian affiliations which will be discussed in Ch. VI. It should be noted that we do not necessarily use the term here in the same way as Professor Broad. It should further be noted that the use of the term here has no reference to the Aristotelean doctrine of categories.

may conveniently express the antithesis of *physis* and *nomos*, as that of the *real* and the *categorial*.  Or again we could speak instead of the '*categorial*,' of the '*Procrustean*,' for the allotting of the world into conventional categories is akin to the activities of the legendary Procrustes.  Later (Ch. xvi) we shall discuss the categorial as the order of '*artifacts*.'[1]

It is the function of the metaphysician to pursue the real. It is Protagoras, and by metaphor Procrustes, who are concerned with the categorial.

We will find that man's relation to Nature has a dual character.  Sometimes he is content to accept and enjoy Nature as it is.  Sometimes, on the other hand, he does not embrace Nature as it is, but instead he creates for himself an artificial structure having contact with Nature at certain points, but being for the most part a sort of shadowy parallel, or substitute, for Nature.  The first is the realm of the real, the second of the categorial.  These categorial systems are partly the creation of individual men, and in part they are the manifestations of society.  They are among the most characteristic possessions of civilised man, and their influence is all pervasive.  Their dominion ranges from modern physics at the one extreme to language and the law at the other.

In the next section of this work we shall first examine the great categorial systems which have been evolved to run parallel to inanimate Nature.  These centre around modern physics.

Then we will examine some of the structures possessed by society rather than by individual men, notably language and the law, categorial structures which take over the functions of Nature in a wide realm.

Finally we will consider the growth of opinion amongst Scholastic philosophers concerning the character of physical science, from the 17th century up to the present day.  This will illustrate the gradual entry of the categorial systems into the perspective of the exponents of the *philosophia perennis*.

[1] It is not to be supposed that all the works of man belong to the categorial order.  That broad field which we describe generically as 'art' is distinguished by the fact that it transcends the categorial and reaches up to the heights of the real order.  (See Ch. IX).

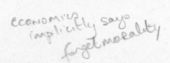
economics implicitly says forget morality

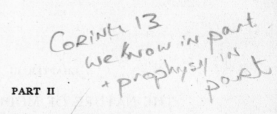

Corinth 13
we know in part
+ prophysy in
part

## PART II

# MAN, SOCIETY, AND NATURE

*The understanding . . . is itself the law-giver of nature.*

IMMANUEL KANT

*The Sun will not overstep his measures ; if he does, the Erinyes, the handmaids of Justice, will find him out.*

HERAKLEITOS

# CHAPTER III

# THE NATURE OF MODERN PHYSICS

*It is not too much to say, I think, that it becomes a matter of doubt whether the structure science builds is solidly based upon the earth, or is a mansion in some Platonic heaven, or is only a kind of castle in the air.*

C. I. LEWIS

*Physics is a practical affair comparable to the art of a clockmaker.*

ALFRED O'RAHILLY

*. . . The universe is passed through a sieve with $3.10^{79}$ holes to render it more comprehensible. In the end what we comprehend about the universe is precisely that which we put into the universe to make it comprehensible.*

SIR ARTHUR EDDINGTON

## The Problem

THE nature of modern physics has become one of the most insistent intellectual questions of our day.[1] A clear understanding of this nature will throw light in many dark places. It might be thought, at first sight, that it would be quite an easy matter to determine its nature. But in fact the opposite is true. In this, physics is not unique. For what is the nature of art, of morals, of life and death, of almost any of our most familiar experiences? A great deal of thought is needed to give satisfactory answers as soon as we become sufficiently self-conscious to realise that there are

---

[1] We use the term 'modern physics' in this work to designate physical science since the Renaissance, as distinct from ancient and medieval physics.

problems here to be solved. We need not be surprised then if we do not find a key at our first attempt to enter the portals of modern physics.

Although we have had modern physics with us now for the last 300 years, attempts in the past to understand it have, on the whole, been casual and desultory, and rather superficial and conventional. It is only in comparatively recent years, with physics and its fruits looming ever larger before us, that really earnest attempts have been made to penetrate the arcana of its nature.

### Aristotelean Science

For Aristotle the pursuit of the various sciences was principally an enquiry pertaining to the real natures of the different natural kinds and species in the world. In other words it concerned the '*physis*' of things, to use the term which ran right through early Greek philosophy, and which signified the unchanging substratum behind the world of becoming.

What we now call BIOLOGY enquired into, and described, the various species of plants and animals and their habits and structures. It was essentially a classificatory science. What we now call PHYSICS included, for Aristotle, the enquiry into the natural kinds and their properties in what we would now call the material world. Like biology, this much at least of physics was essentially classificatory. As it turned out, physics was a much less fruitful pursuit than biology, perhaps because the real kinds in the world of physics were not so diverse and clearly demarcated as in biology.

It should be noted that Aristotelean science only *pertained* to the essences of things. It did not claim actually to penetrate to the essence itself, except in such special cases as that of geometrical figures, and of man whose essence is rational animality. In the case of other natural kinds what was determined were the characteristic properties. But these in turn were considered to spring from and manifest as it were, the underlying essence, even though this itself was inaccessible.[1]

[1] See e.g. Joyce, G. H. : *Principles of Logic* (London, 1908), p. 154.

Consequently Aristotelean science was, in its intention at least, ultimately bound to the real nature of things, to the *physis*.[1]

Thus for Aristotle physics is continuous with metaphysics. *In principle* the science and philosophy of matter are one and the same.

A modern writer sums up the Aristotelean programme thus:

Aristotle held that every existing individual was what it was by reason of its essence or inner ground. Hence we can have scientific knowledge of an existing individual only when we are able to trace the connection of the contents of that individual with its essence. The scientist or philosopher attains truth when he analyses and re-synthesises an individual in such a way as to make clear the inner necessity that links the sensible accidents of that individual with its essence. He is started on this quest by observing facts of experience. These facts, inasmuch as they are merely known to happen, belong to the world of opinion not to the world of science. But their happening suggests to the scientist or philosopher a problem : the problem of demonstrating a necessary connection between the observed fact and the essence. The solution of this kind of problem involves both induction and deduction : induction for the purpose of discovering essences and first principles ; deduction for the purpose of converting a mere conjunction of fact into a rational connection. Should our scientist or philosopher succeed in demonstrating this rational connection, his conclusion is scientific or philosophic ; *he knows not merely that the fact happens but also why it must happen*.[2]

Aristotelean sciences were cultivated with great vigour right through the Middle Ages up to the Renaissance. At the Renaissance some of the sciences broke away violently from the Aristotelean ideals. Others of the sciences, however, did not undergo any fundamental change of character.

---

[1] cf. Aristotle : *Physics*, 194[b], ' How far then must the physicist know the form or essence ? Up to a point, perhaps, as the doctor must know sinew or the smith bronze. . . .' On the other hand it is the business of the primary type of philosophy, or metaphysics, to penetrate as far into the essence as possible ; it does not stop short as does physics. We may remark here that in *Physics*, 193[b] Aristotle makes the pregnant distinction between the physicist on the one hand and the mathematician or astronomer on the other (See Appendix).

[2] O'Neill, J. : *Cosmology* (London, 1924), p. 16.

The biological sciences, for instance, have retained their general Aristotelean character up to the present day. They have made great strides, but yet they are still in the main descriptive and classificatory. They are still rooted in the real natures of the plants and animals. They still pertain fundamentally to the *physis*.

## The New Physical Science

While the biological sciences remained fundamentally unchanged, other sciences were transformed. The outward manifestation of this transformation is best seen in physical science. From the 17th century onwards physics took wings. It grew at a prodigious and ever-increasing pace until today it is a vast structure of amazing scope and intricacy. Physics is the premier modern science, and other sciences have followed in its wake. This rapid growth of physical science was accompanied by a pervasive change of character. The atmosphere and 'feel' of the post-Renaissance physics are fundamentally different from those of the older Aristotelean physics.

The characteristic feature of the new sciences was a type of extreme empiricism. A cleavage appeared between the old philosophy and the new empirical sciences. O'Neill writes:

In every branch of knowledge, empirical science became divorced from metaphysical science: each was cultivated by different men and along different lines. Thus topic after topic of the Aristotelean Encyclopaedia—hitherto the preserve of medieval theologians and philosophers—was taken over and made the object of one or other of the ever-growing branches of modern science: moreover these topics were treated after a fashion wholly unknown to Aristotle and the School, and in many instances blossomed out into sciences that horrified the upholders of traditional learning.[1]

New philosophies arose, too, opposing the philosophy of the Schoolmen, and professing to be grounded on the new sciences. The science and philosophy of matter were again identified, but this time from the opposite direction, for now the science

[1] *Ibid.* p. 19.

precedes the philosophy. The philosophy depends upon the science, instead of *vice versa*, as had formerly been the case. In other words *the new sciences are autonomous*. They pursue their own paths. They are their own masters. This is the most significant feature of the new sciences, and it is of the utmost importance to understand it clearly.

Confining our attention now to physics, the prototype science, let us ask a fundamental question:

*What precisely happened in the 17th century to physical science to give it this new character and this new lease of life?*

Professor Collingwood remarks, in his *Autobiography*, that only a very learned man or a very ignorant man would attempt to give a brief answer to this question. While not aspiring to the first rôle, and endeavouring to avoid the second, we may yet perhaps be able to lighten the darkness with a taper, if not with the full light of day. This chapter will be concerned in the main with presenting the rudiments of what seems to be, on the whole, the most satisfactory theory, namely the categorial Procrustean theory of the nature of modern physics. This theory, let it be remarked, arises primarily from an examination of the internal structure of post-Renaissance physics itself, and does not come from the dictates of any *a priori* principle.

This Procrustean theory is of comparatively recent origin. Since the 17th century many attempts have been made to explain the nature of the new science, based on various lines of approach. In later chapters we will discuss some of these earlier schools of thought, and will show, too, how the Procrustean theory had long been foreshadowed, although for the most part only in the germ and not explicitly.

To make the situation clearer we will first consider the classical 'realist' theory of physics, the theory from which the exponents of the Procrustean theory broke away.

### The Classical, or Realist, Theory of Modern Physics

The classical writers on scientific method, men like John Stuart Mill, and the English empiricists generally, took it for granted that modern physics was, like ancient physics, endeavouring to discover the nature and functioning of the physical world about us. Only, they believed, it was doing it much more successfully than was the ancient and medieval physics. They saw the change that came over physics in the days of Galileo as a change occasioned by increased attention to observation and experiment. They accused the Aristoteleans of paying too little attention to observation and too much to *a priori* notions. Liberation from the medieval strait-jacket, and careful experiment and measurement, coupled with the powerful instrument of mathematics, was believed to be the reason for the great strides forward in physical science from Galileo onward.

Physics was thus regarded as a truly empirical science. The physicist was supposed to observe uniformities in Nature and to generalise these into laws. Some varied this a little by pointing out that physicists make hypotheses and then put them to the test of experiment. If experiment verifies the hypothesis then we have discovered a valid law or theory of physics. By these means, it was believed, were discovered such laws and principles as Newton's Laws of Motion and The Law of Universal Gravitation, the Conservation of Energy, the Wave Theory of Light, the Atomic Theory of Matter, and so on.

Physics was thus held by these philosophers and logicians to be slowly wresting out the secrets of Nature, to be steadily unfolding before us the constitution of the physical world. The uniformity of Nature is revealed in the true laws of physics, and renders them immutable.

Physics is subject at every turn to the test of experiment, and anyone can upset a theory simply by showing that some observation is contrary to it. Thus physics abhors authority and anything that smacks of the *a priori*. Consequently the modern physicist reviles the old Aristotelean physicist who, he believes, was bound hand and foot by authority and *a priori* notions.

By this slow empirical advance, it was believed, there was built up the great edifice of modern physics; an edifice which today occupies one of the most prominent positions in our intellectual horizon, while in practical applications it has transformed daily life by surrounding us with a countless multiplicity of instruments and amenities.

Although the classical empiricist logicians were not all agreed on what was, precisely, the scientific method, yet on the general picture they were unanimous.[1]

### The Eddingtonian Theory

Nevertheless there has long been a minority which has held other views about the nature of physics and scientific method. In recent years these views have pushed their way more and more to the fore. The revolt has been rather tentative up to the present, but in this chapter we will extend it further and develop its consequences.

The John the Baptist of the Movement was Immanuel Kant. In more recent times the principles were revived by Poincaré.[2] But the new interpretation has received its greatest impetus from the works of the late Professor Eddington, who gave a most elegant expression to what others had long been struggling to articulate. The new approach is based on the mode of acquiring knowledge in experimental physics. It pays little attention to what the physicist *says*, but much attention to what he *does*. It looks away from the world to the activity of the physicist himself. To Eddington and his school of thought, the laws of physics are subjective, arbitrary, conventional, dogmatic, and authoritarian. This is, of course, precisely the reverse of the classical theory which believes the laws to be supremely objective. But the new theory holds that *the laws of physics are not the laws of Nature but the laws of the physicists*. The laws of physics are always true, not because they represent uniformities of Nature, but simply because the physicist never lets them be untrue.

[1] See further Ch. XI, on Scientific Method.
[2] Some account of the various transitional theories will be found in later chapters, notably in Ch. XVIII in the Section on Modern Physics and Scholastic Philosophy.

Newton wrote in the *Principia* that 'Nature is pleased with simplicity and affects not the pomp of superfluous causes.' The classical empiricist logician would heartily endorse this dictum, although he might be puzzled if asked how he knew it to be true. But the alternative view would insist that *it is not Nature which is pleased with simplicity, but the physicist.* Whether Nature is pleased with simplicity or not we cannot tell, at least not within the province of experimental science. But we do know that the physicist is pleased with simplicity and will exercise all his ingenuity to achieve it. The simplicity of the laws of physics, then, tells us much about the physicist, but nothing immediately about Nature.

This reorientation towards physics can be expressed very neatly by using the parable of Procrustes, and saying that physics is a PROCRUSTEAN BED. Procrustes lived in ancient Greece. He was a brigand who terrorised Attica until finally he was vanquished by Theseus. Now Procrustes had a bed, and it was his practice to make travellers conform in length to that bed. If they were too short he stretched them out until they fitted, and if they were too long he chopped off their legs until they were the right length.

This is a parable of what the physicist does with Nature. He makes Nature conform to what he wants, and having done so announces that he has discovered a law of Nature : namely that all the travellers fit the bed. Hence it is that the laws of physics are always true. It is because the physicist makes Nature conform to them. He runs Nature out into moulds, so to speak. *A law of physics is not something discovered in Nature, but something imposed upon Nature.*

In brief, physics is a put-up job. The physicist puts it all in implicitly at the beginning, and then draws it out explicitly at the end. Physics is manufactured, not discovered.

Eddington puts the matter in his own inimitable style[1] :

Procrustes, you will remember, stretched or chopped down his guests to fit the bed he had constructed. But perhaps you have not heard the rest of the story. He measured them up before they

[1] Eddington, A. S. : *The Philosophy of Physical Science* (Cambridge, 1939), p. 109.

left next morning, and wrote a learned paper 'On the Uniformity of Stature of Travellers' for the Anthropological Society of Attica.

This parable, when fully understood, gets right to the heart of modern physics. It is immensely illuminating.

The way in which the process is introduced into the laboratory is put by Eddington thus:

The kind of observation on which physical theory is based is not a casual taking notice of things around us, nor a general running round with a measuring rod. *Under cover of the term " good " observation the bed of Procrustes is artfully concealed.*[1]

This will strike home to anyone trained in a physical laboratory. It should wake him from his dogmatic slumbers if anything can.

Eddington goes on :

Suppose an artist puts forward the fantastic theory that the form of a human head exists in a rough shaped block of marble. All our rational instinct is roused against such an anthropomorphic speculation. It is inconceivable that Nature should have placed such a form inside the block. But the artist proceeds to verify his theory experimentally—with quite rudimentary apparatus too. Merely using a chisel to separate the form for our inspection, he triumphantly proves his theory. Was it in this way that Rutherford rendered concrete the nucleus which his scientific imagination had created ?

Physics acquired this character in the 17th century with the commencement of systematic experiment and measurement. For *systematic* experiment leads easily into this Procrustean procedure. At first the Procrustean element was very small. But it grew apace until in modern times the system is almost entirely Procrustean.

Far from being grounded on the simple observation of Nature, which the old Aristotelean physics was, or was intended to be, the new physics is highly sophisticated and artificial. Modern physics means discipline and authority. A training in physics is a training in this discipline. The student of experimental physics is trained in the laboratory in the methods of making Nature fit the Procrustean beds laid down by the great

[1] *Ibid.* p. 110.

physicists. This is the meaning of the familiar 'practical work' in the laboratory. The teacher in an elementary physical laboratory can hardly be oblivious to the points of resemblance between his function and that of the sergeant-major on a military parade-ground. Ultimately the teacher is called upon to say in effect, 'You must do this and that or I will not approve,' i.e. 'You must make Nature fit the Procrustean beds made out by our predecessors, the great physicists, or you will not be a good physicist yourself.' This is done, as Eddington says, under the guise of insisting on 'good' observations.

These rules are particularly stringent for junior members of the craft. Sometimes a senior member succeeds in showing that there is some new and better way of moulding Nature, and if he can convince the scientific world at large of its efficacy, he will be the author of a new law or theory. On the analogy of the parade-ground this would be something like a new and superior drill movement being worked out. Even military drill books change occasionally.[1]

## The Pragmatic Goal

Modern physics seen in this light has a pragmatic basis. It is not, like the old pre-Renaissance physics, an enquiry into the real. It has a different aim: *it is the forging of a practical instrument of prediction.* The justification of a law of physics, or of a physical theory,[2] is its usefulness in prediction of events. *The ability to predict is the final court of appeal.* It overrides all else. The truth of these contentions is to be seen if we examine the actual *practice* of the physicist as distinct from any discourse the physicist may utter.

## Procrustes at Work

As far as practice is concerned it would hardly be an exaggeration to say that the physicist holds on to a law of

[1] cf. Eddington (*ibid.* p. 113): 'The boy who outrageously breaks the rules of a game may be suitably punished by his companions, or he may be commemorated as the founder of Rugby football.'

[2] It is neither possible nor desirable to make any sharp demarcation between 'laws' and 'theories' of physics.

physics until he gets tired of it. To him it is a tool which he can use when he pleases, and discard when he pleases. Having discarded one theory he can pick up another, or perhaps even use the two at once, as has happened on more than one occasion. His choice is determined by his own habits and convenience. As a rule no single experiment can establish a law of physics on any firm basis, i.e. provide a compelling reason for the physicist to recognise it. Similarly no single experiment can ever demolish a theory, i.e. compel the physicist to relinquish it there and then. This, of course, is quite at variance with the classical theory of the science.

Let us take a typical example and see to which pattern it conforms. The corpuscular theory of light in the hands of Newton was a fairly satisfactory theory of the nature of light. But with increasing interest in the phenomena of optical interference it became more and more difficult and troublesome to hold the corpuscular theory, while the wave theory became more and more attractive. No single experiment could finally demolish the corpuscular theory. It was only necessary to introduce more and more auxiliary hypotheses and the corpuscular theory, and its interpretation of the phenomena, could have been retained indefinitely. But in time most physicists came to feel that it was not worth while, that it had become too cumbersome. They grew tired of the corpuscular theory, and early in the 19th century they turned to what had by then become the much simpler wave theory, and thenceforth interpreted the phenomena in terms of the latter.

However, at the end of the 19th century and the beginning of the 20th century, with new discoveries, a greatly modified corpuscular theory was revived under the name of the quantum theory. The quantum theory and the wave theory were employed conjointly for a number of years until finally both were subsumed into the theory of 'wave mechanics.'

Throughout the history of the theories of light there is very little of the 'observing uniformities and generalising them into laws,' and very much of the physicist as the master operating successive Procrustean beds.

A particularly striking case of the *a priori* nature of physical theories and laws is provided by the particle known as the neutrino. In the beta-particle decay of radio-active nuclei, a continuous spectrum of beta-rays is emitted. This continuous spectrum provides one of the major problems of contemporary physics. A consideration of the process shows that either the classical laws of the conservation of energy and angular momentum are not obeyed by individual nuclei, or else another particle, hitherto unknown, which Fermi called the 'neutrino,' is emitted along with the electron. This new particle is given just the spin and energy needed to make up the discrepancies, but it will have no charge and practically no mass. Consequently its detection would be difficult by any direct means. Nevertheless most physicists follow Fermi in postulating the neutrino, simply because it saves the conservation laws. It is quite *ad hoc*, but it prevents the laws being violated. The physicist's Procrustean rôle is quite apparent. *It is clearly the physicist who is imposing the conservation laws and making Nature fit, and not vice versa as the older logicians thought.*

It is the same throughout physics: the physicist is the law-giver. He makes and imposes the laws, and has power to enforce them or withdraw them as he sees fit.

Again, reverting to the early days of modern physics, we may ask: how did Galileo know that in the absence of resistance to motion all bodies would fall towards the Earth with the same acceleration? How did Newton know his laws of motion to be true; in particular, that every body continues in its state of rest or of uniform motion in a straight line unless compelled by external force to change that state? Did Galileo and Newton discover these laws or invent them? Are they 'natural' or Procrustean? When we consider the matter we are driven to put them in the latter category.

Galileo can hold to his contention as long as he pleases by attributing departures from equal acceleration to resistances to motion. But how do we know there is a resistance to motion? By reduced acceleration! Similarly Newton preserves his first law by attributing any departure from uniform rectilinear motion to an impressed force. But how do we know when there is such a force? By observing a departure from uniform rectilinear motion!

On this procedure it is impossible ever to disprove the laws so long as physicists choose to retain them[1].

Try to grasp the laws intellectually, as laws of Nature, and we are in a vicious circle from which there is no escape. Regard them as Procrustean beds and their function is clear.

Let us turn now from particular theories to a wider horizon. Here we will find some illuminating situations.

One instance which must give everyone food for thought is the case of the American physicist, D. C. Miller. It is well known that one of the strongest experimental grounds for the special theory of relativity is the Michelson-Morley experiment performed in the year 1887. This celebrated experiment was designed to detect the motion of the earth through the ether. The result was *negative*. No relative motion could be detected. The negative result of this experiment has become fundamental to a great deal of modern physics.

But the interesting sequel is that since then Miller has made an exhaustive investigation, and has persistently achieved *positive* results in his repetition of the principle of the Michelson-Morley experiment.[2] However his has been a voice crying in the wilderness, for the physicists have heeded him not. Special relativity is so firmly entrenched that any fundamental change at this stage is unthinkable. In other words special relativity has hardened into a Procrustean bed to which physicists are clinging tenaciously, and in terms of which they are interpreting the world. The physicists are not inclined to give up their bed at present, Miller or no Miller.

As a final instance, let us point to the national divergences in physics. The patterns of physics are not entirely unanimous and universal. They differ, in fact, from country to country. E.g., in electromagnetic theory the Continental physicists have tended to describe phenomena in terms basically of Coulomb's

---

[1] Cf. Ch. X on the alleged non-existence of badgers.
[2] See Miller, D. C.: *Reviews of Modern Physics*, 5, 203, (1933).

inverse square law of force between electric charges and between magnetic poles.  But, on the other hand, the English physicists have generally preferred to picture electric and magnetic phenomena in terms of the lines of force in the medium, as envisaged by the powerful pictorial imagination of Michael Faraday.  For elementary physics these two treatments give identical results, as was pointed out long ago by Clerk Maxwell.[1]  But for advanced theory they by no means work out identically.[2]

The English and Continental physicists thus, traditionally, follow two quite different patterns in their electromagnetic theory.  They are running two different Procrustean beds.

Such illustrations as these could be multiplied almost indefinitely.  But, with such examples as we have before us, it should be clear that the simple theory that physics consists of generalising from observation, whether of events occurring naturally or brought about by experiment, is much too facile. It makes the physicist a *passive* receptacle.  It leaves out of account the *activity* of the physicist.

The theory of hypotheses is slightly more enlightened.  It gets in some of the physicist's activity, but it still regards him as exploring the world before him objectively.  It leaves out of account the all-important fact of his *formative* activity, whereby he not merely explores the world, but forms, manufactures, as it were, a world of his own design.[3]

This omission is rectified in the Procrustean theory, which alone does full justice to the situation.

### Hyper-Physics

With such considerations as these in mind, Professor Eddington claimed to be able to foreshadow what the physicist will discover, by looking at the methods by which he will set about his task.  He relates a parable about a fisherman and his net.  The fisherman goes out into the sea and draws his net

[1] Clerk Maxwell, J. : *Treatise on Electricity and Magnetism* (London, 1873), Preface.
[2] See e.g. O'Rahilly, A.: *Electromagnetics* (London, 1938).
[3] We shall see later (Ch. VI), that the recognition of this formative activity is due originally to Kant, and is the starting-point of his philosophy.

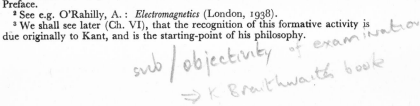

through the waters and catches a shoal of fish, which he brings back to land and examines. But a man sitting on the seashore could foretell, before the fisherman puts out to sea, quite a lot about the size of the fish in the catch, simply by inspecting the mesh of the net. If the fisherman had dragged a different kind of net through the sea he would have obtained a different catch.

By looking at the net which the physicist drags through the world, Eddington has attempted to tell beforehand what the physicist is going to find. This constitutes what we might call a '*hyper-physics*' or a '*transcendental physics*.' By this means, and without any experiment, the armchair physicist can make quite remarkable predictions. Eddington, for instance, has calculated what he claims to be the total number of electrons in the universe. He arrives at the number $136.2^{256}$, with the same number of protons. Of course he has not counted them, but, as he writes:

Our ability to predict the number of protons and electrons in the universe implies that the number is imposed by the procedure followed in analysing the inter-relatedness of our experience into a manifestation of an assemblage of particles or wave systems. It is a commonplace that electrons are not intrinsically distinguishable from one another ; it is therefore not surprising that the total number allowed for in our scheme of dissection of phenomena depends on the conventional distinctions introduced when, for example, we decide that a certain diffuse wave packet is composed of two electrons rather than one.[1]

The possibility of this hyper-physics is not quite so novel as it might seem at first sight. For the familiar process of dimensional analysis gives a remarkable amount of informa-tion with a minimum of experimental knowledge.[2] E.g. the armchair physicist, by quite a simple process, can derive the *form* of the expression for the period of the simple pendulum in terms of the length of the string and the acceleration of

---

[1] Eddington, A. S. : *Relativity Theory of Protons and Electrons* (Cambridge, 1936), p. 316.
[2] The theory of the dimensional homogeneity of the equations of physics, on which the process of dimensional analysis rests, was laid down by Fourier in 1822, in his great work : *Théorie Analytique de la Chaleur.* An account of the subject will be found in any elementary work on physics. More advanced accounts will be found in special monographs, e.g. Bridgman, P. W. : *Dimensional Analysis* (Yale, 1931).

gravity, and this without knowing anything of Newton's laws of motion, or indeed having any explicit theory of dynamics. Dimensional analysis gets behind the particular theories of the detailed processes at work, and considers the form of the structure which we have imposed on the world. *In this case we have imposed the form by our mere definitions of the quantities of elementary dynamics—mass, length, time, period, acceleration, etc.*

The process of dimensional analysis has long been familiar to physicists. It has been pressed into service in a great variety of physical problems. It is used extensively by engineers for problems which are too difficult to be solved by ordinary means, as, for instance, the Froude analysis of the wave-making resistance of ships.

The dimensional method does not give us full information. It gives the form of the relation without the numerical constants. For instance, in the case of the pendulum, the dimensional analysis tells us that

$$\tau \propto \sqrt{\frac{l}{g}}$$

The full expression, deduced dynamically, is

$$\tau = 2\pi \sqrt{\frac{l}{g}}$$

The definitions of our basic quantities have determined the expression *a priori* except for the numerical factor $2\pi$.

Dimensional analysis is a considerable step towards a hyper-physics. Its familiarity to the practising physicist should pave the way towards an acceptance of the much more comprehensive Eddingtonian hyper-physics. For Eddington's theories have been thought novel and strange, and have been greeted sceptically by many on the ground that physics is a simple experimental science, and that consequently we cannot possibly predict the things Eddington claims to predict *a priori*.

But dimensional analysis, which is accepted on all hands, must give pause to the naïve assertion that physics is a pure experimental science, for it gives us an amazing amount of information *a priori*. Dimensional analysis is a prelude to the Eddingtonian theory, and provides strong support for the Procrustean theory of physics in general, which is of course a theory of the *a priori*.

Perhaps the following passage, in which Eddington sums up the situation, will be more comprehensible in the light of these remarks.

. . . There is nothing in the whole system of laws of physics that cannot be deduced unambiguously from epistemological considerations. An intelligence, unacquainted with our universe, but acquainted with the system of thought by which the human mind interprets to itself the content of its sensory experience, should be able to attain all the knowledge of physics that we have attained by experiment. He would not deduce the particular events and objects of our experience, but he would deduce the generalisations we have based on them. For example, he would infer the existence and properties of radium, but not the dimensions of the earth.

The mind which tried to apprehend simultaneously the complexity of the universe would be overwhelmed. Experience must be dealt with in bits ; then a system must be devised for re-connecting the bits ; and so on. One outcome of this treatment is that the universe is passed through a sieve with $3.10^{79}$ holes to render it more comprehensible. *In the end what we comprehend about the universe is precisely that which we put into the universe to make it comprehensible.*

. . . We may look forward with undiminished enthusiasm to learning in the coming years what lies hidden in the atomic nucleus —even though we suspect it is hidden there by ourselves.[1]

## Generalising the Procrustean Theory

Eddington has drawn attention to the *a priori* and ' artificial ' character of the theories of physics. Now we can carry this principle further to the conclusion that not only the theories of modern physics, but the whole subject matter of modern physics, the entities and elements of modern physics, are subjective, *a priori*, artificial, and conventional.

The *a priori* character of a law of physics, e.g. the conservation of energy, is obviously shared by such an entity as the

[1] Eddington, A. S. : *Relativity Theory of Protons and Electrons*, pp. 327 f.

neutrino which we discussed above. The neutrino might be described as a mnemonic, or shorthand way of saying things; *What things, are determined by us.*[1]

So too with the other entities of physics : the electron, the proton, electric and magnetic fields, gravitation, and so on : They are all mnemonics, or interpretative principles, or Procrustean beds. They are our own creations, and their justification is utilitarian.

While this much would be conceded by many physicists today, it seems to be still generally believed that at least in its elements physics does deal in fact with such things as space and time and so on. But, as we shall see, modern physics in reality has nothing directly to do with space, time, matter, force, energy, etc. Certainly these names are employed, but it is a delusion to think that the entities themselves are there. It is a delusion which has undoubtedly hampered the growth of physics a great deal during the last few centuries, and has been a source of much confusion.

What we call 'space,' 'time,' and 'mass,' are the familiar triumvirate on which mechanics, at least, is ostensibly built. The other branches of physics : electricity, heat, etc., have, historically, been developed by adding to the so-called space, time, and mass, other new entities which have been given such names as electric charge, quantity of heat, and so on.

Although all these natural names were, and are still, employed, a careful examination shows that *it is impossible to give a rational account of the elements of modern physics in natural terms.*

## Mass

Let us consider first of all the case of mass. Newton described ' mass ' as the amount of matter in the body. Hence the physicist was supposed to be dealing with matter under

---

[1] It is important to remember the fact that the various things to be embraced by the mnemonic are, in part at least, determined by the physicist. The data of the physicist, for which mnemonics are constructed, are *not* simple given phenomena. Our Procrustean activity transforms everything it touches. Ernst Mach, too (p. 206), held that these entities are mnemonics or 'mental artifices,' but he held this in conjunction with the belief that the physicist was *passive*. We, on the contrary, hold him to be *active*. (See Ch. XVIII).

the property of mass. It was not until Ernst Mach published his great work : *Die Mechanik in ihrer Entwickelung* (Engl. tr. *The Science of Mechanics*), in the 80's of the last century, that any serious criticism was levelled at this dogma. In that work Mach drew attention to the barrenness for physics of the account of mass as the amount of matter in the body. He succeeded furthermore in showing that all other proposed definitions of mass were either trivial or circular. The well known text book procedure might be recalled to mind. The usual plan is to define mass in terms of force in one chapter, and then, in the next chapter, to define force in terms of mass. This is obviously circular.

Mach himself proposed a rather elaborate kinematic 'definition' of mass, but it, too, is far from satisfactory, and is highly artificial.

Indeed, the situation is that we can say very little more about mass than that it is a constant associated with the body. *It is 'm' in theoretical physics.* And, going further, in view of the Lorentz transformation for mass, it is not even a constant, but depends on the relative velocity between body and observer.

*Mass started its career with Newton, representing matter. It is now a highly abstract mathematical function.* And with its withdrawal into the upper realms matter faded out of modern physics. Today the term 'matter' in physics is a curious relic, used more by courtesy than anything else. There is no compelling reason why the name 'matter' should be used at all in physics in these days of wave mechanics. The very slight connotation which the term still conveys to the physicist could quite well be expressed in other and less ambiguous terms.

Thus modern physics has exorcised from its household a phantom : matter.

### Space and Time

What of space and time ? Just as with Newton modern physics started with matter, and then gradually drifted away from it, *m* taking over its functions, so modern physics started in the days of Galileo with space and time.   But these, like matter, were no more than the starting points.   *The development of experimental and mathematical physics involved a withdrawal from the real world of space and time, just as it did from the real world of matter.*   Physics soon developed mathematical functions *s* and *t* which it moulded to suit its purposes.   But the *names* 'space' and 'time' persisted as a trap for the unwary.

It is only necessary to trace through the attempted definition of 'time' found in physics to-day, to see that 'time,' like 'mass,' has departed widely from its real prototype.   Probably the best attempt at defining time in physics is by means of the criterion of a number of independent 'uniform periodic processes.'   If a number of such processes keep in step with one another, the common 'time' so measured is taken as normative.

But even this criterion gives only a rather dubious probability of constancy.   In practice it is necessary to be more positive, and to define the time sequence in some arbitrary manner, e.g. by the oscillation of a quartz crystal, quite unconnected with whatever rational or intuitive knowledge of real time we might possess.   If any doubt were left a consideration of the Lorentz transformation for time provides ample confirmation that *the 't' of the mathematical physicist cannot be regarded as being in any way representative of that entity 'time' of which we are all aware.*   '*t*' is no longer anchored to real time.   It is now a mathematical function at the complete disposal of the physicist.

Similar considerations apply to space or length.

The fact that it is now quite widely recognised that modern physics does not deal in any immediate way through mass with matter, whereas the delusion about space and time is persistent, is no doubt partly due to the historical accident that Newton called *m* not 'matter' but 'mass,' whereas *s* and *t* were left with the misnomers 'space' and 'time.' Hence the confusion was perpetuated.

It would be much better to speak, in modern physics, not of 'space' and 'time' but to use some coined words, or perhaps more simply, to say the '*s* function' and the '*t* function.'

*Other Physical Quantities*

Concerning the physicists' so-called 'force,' 'work,' 'energy,' and so on, their translation into the abstract realms can easily be traced out by the reader.[1]

As for the entities in branches of physics other than mechanics, entities such as 'quantity of heat,' 'electric charge,' 'electric potential,' and so on, little need be said. Their artificial character is quite apparent. 'Quantity of heat' is an arbitrary definition founded to some extent on our common thermal experience. But 'quantity of electricity' and 'electric potential' are quite unconnected with common experience, and are from first to last the arbitrary creations of the physicist. They serve him as instruments and chattels.

*The Physicist and the Philosopher*

This account of *m*, *s*, and *t* in physical science should serve to settle disputes between metaphysicians and physicists about matter, space, and time. A generation ago, when 'relativity' was prominently before the public eye, disputes about space and time between the philosophers and the relativity physicists were well nigh interminable. But the considerations put forward here show that such disputes are baseless. The parties were, all unknowingly, discussing different things. The mistaken belief that the physicists are talking about the real space, time, and matter of the metaphysicians, arises in part because the physicists still use these *names*, but without the literal reality.

A recent writer on electromagnetic theory, J. A. Stratton,[2]

---

[1] An example of the absurd results of the failure to realise this translation into an artificial world is given by Susan Stebbing in her excellent little work *Philosophy and the Physicists* (London, 1937), pp. 274–5. In theoretical physics there is a technical term, 'action', which means the product of the momentum and the distance, or more strictly $\int m v \, ds$. It is an abstract mathematical function which has assumed considerable importance in mathematical physics.

This quantity was taken literally by a philosophical writer, because of the name 'action,' to indicate that the world shows some sort of urge to self-completion.

That such misunderstandings occur is partly the fault of the physicist because of his apparently ineradicable habit of taking a common term and using it to refer to some abstract mathematical function.

[2] Stratton, J. A. : *Electromagnetic Theory* (New York, 1941). It is refreshing to find the author of a text-book adopting this point of view, for text-books are generally the home of hide-bound convention.

approaches his subject in somewhat the spirit of the foregoing. Stratton commences: 'By an electromagnetic field let us understand the domain of the four vectors E and B, D and H.' He does not attempt to draw a red herring across the trail in the traditional manner by professing to derive these entities, E, B, D and H, in some way from Nature. He is frank enough to say from the start that his subject is the domain of E, B, D and H (a domain, we might say, of mental '*artifacts*.'[1]) He leaves it to the sequel to give what *pragmatic* reasons he can find for inducing people to take an interest in the domain of E, B, D and H. Stratton puts a completely arbitrary system before us. When we ask Why? What is it all about? What is the good of it? he will answer by pointing to its pragmatic sanctions, in so far as he may be able. And the pragmatic sanction is its power of co-ordination and prediction. The system does not profess to tell us anything immediately about the nature of the real world.

Stratton's mode of casting physics might well serve as a model for other writers. It would banish much of the present obscurity.

If we wish to sum up modern physics in a phrase, we could call it '*a priori pragmatism*.' This is a far cry from the old classical empiricist doctrine, which professed to build up from Nature. In fact it is precisely the reverse, since it makes contact with 'Nature' not at the beginning, but at the end.[2]

Let us carry on Stratton's principles, and say: 'the world of modern physics is the domain of the artifacts $m$, $s$, $t$, F, E, B, D, H, etc., etc.' This leaves open the question of the relation of this world of artifacts to the real world. This is for the philosopher to determine, not the physicist.

---

[1] On artifacts, see Ch. XVI.

[2] It is here that the deductive system of modern physics and the deductive system of Plato in the central Books of the *Republic* differ so fundamentally, in spite of a superficial resemblance. For with Plato the first principle, the Form of the Good, is grasped intellectually and intuitively. Consequently the whole hierarchical system is supremely grounded on Nature at the beginning. There is nothing of this in the hierarchical system of modern physics, where the sanction is always at the extremities not at the apex.

*The Teaching of Modern Physics*

One of the greatest obstacles to understanding this Procrustean pragmatic point of view is the manner in which elementary physics is still taught. The authors of elementary text books persist in trying to derive the bases of mechanics in some way from Nature, in accordance with the classical empiricist theory of physics. This leaves the student puzzled as to how, for instance, Newton could know that his laws of motion are true, since the arguments given to make them 'natural' are rather weak. If he is of an enquiring turn of mind he will eventually find it an insoluble problem: how to disentangle mass, force, etc., and define each of them 'naturally.' In the end, on this system, the student is merely beaten into conformity, whether he feels it right or not.

All this difficulty confronting the alert student would be eliminated if physics were presented from the start as an artificial system, with a justification in success, on the model of Stratton's presentation of the electromagnetic theory. There would then no longer be intellectual difficulties about the commencement. Constant reference to the historical development of modern physics would remove the initial strangeness of such a system.

*The Universal Applicability of the Theories of Physics*

The classical empiricist logicians, and the physicists who echoed their views, were generally rather puzzled when asked how they knew that the laws of physics are true always and in all places. How did they know that the present laws of physics held millions of years ago? or would hold millions of years to come? The validity of the laws in the remote past was assumed by cosmologists concerned with the origin of the Universe, and physicists were fond of speculations about the remote future, e.g. of the ultimate effect of the second law of thermodynamics. Similarly in the region of the distant stars, how did physicists know our laws applied? Physicists did not hesitate to *use* the laws in all these circumstances, but they were somewhat diffident about explaining why. To them, when they thought about it at all, it seemed that they were face to face with the problem of induction, which, in these remote realms of time and space, clamoured for an answer with particular insistence.

However, with our altered point of view, we see that the problem is not such an urgent one for the physicist after all. For what he is doing is just interpreting the world in remote times and places in terms of his principles. He can give us his results for what they may be worth. In *insisting* on them he is simply being firm about his system in a rather naïve manner.

The physicist is not in any specially urgent way compelled to answer the induction problem in order to make his cosmological conclusions intelligible. Not that the induction problem does not need solution. Far from it. But the physicist in these circumstances is no more concerned with it than usual.[1]

In a different direction, we may consider the attitude commonly adopted by physicists to psychical phenomena. Official physics, as represented for instance by the Editor of *Nature*, has traditionally adopted a lordly attitude to psychical phenomena. 'These things can't happen' say the physicists. But in the light of our Procrustean principles we can see that what they really mean is : 'we, as physicists, refuse to take account of these alleged phenomena. They are outside our terms of reference, and hence we officially exclude them from the columns of *Nature*.' This is practically all that the physicist is entitled to say. *He cannot genuinely lay down the law about psychic phenomena.*[2]

---

[1] Note that the Procrustean principles lose their charter when any break, singularity, or intervention occurs ; i.e. in the case of miracles.

[2] cf. Broad, C. D. : *The Mind and its Place in Nature*, p. viii. ' I shall no doubt be blamed by certain scientists, and, I am afraid, by some philosophers, for having taken serious account of the alleged facts which are investigated by Psychical Researchers. I am wholly impenitent about this. The scientists in question seem to me to confuse the Author of Nature with the Editor of *Nature* ; or, at any rate, to suppose that there can be no productions of the former which would not be accepted for publication by the latter. And I see no reason to believe this.'

In fairness to *Nature*, it should be added that this excellent journal in recent years has taken a more conciliatory attitude to psychical research.

We could go on adding example to example of the effects immediately touching physicists of the reorientation to physics ; but these should suffice.

### The Autonomy of Physics

One of the most striking features of post-Renaissance physics, and indeed of modern science generally, is its autonomy. It is a law unto itself, as its history shows, and it brooks no interference from outside, from philosophers, or theologians, or anyone else. This autonomy has tended to be a source of puzzlement since the 17th century. For if physics is investigating Nature, then we would expect physics to be closely linked with other enquiries into the nature of things. But physics persisted in following its own course, whether this clashed with other branches of knowledge or not.

On the Procrustean interpretation of modern physics, however, the puzzle is solved. For now we see in physics not an investigation into the nature of things, in company with investigations from other aspects, but a thoroughly artificial[1] system, and hence one which is rightly independent and autonomous. Its function is to give prediction and control, and it never comes into immediate contact with enquiries into the nature of things. It is in fact a science of mental 'artifacts.'

This is a subject about which we shall have more to say elsewhere.[2]

### A Plurality of Physics

We saw that modern physics is the domain of the artifacts $s$, $t$, $m$, F, E, B, D, H, etc. Physics is thus highly artificial and abstract. This being so, it is possible, further, to conceive of any number of fundamentally different systems of physics generated by making different primary selections. The direction which physics actually took was determined in the early formative period by Galileo and Newton and their contemporaries. Just why physics took the course it did, and not

[1] Using the term 'artificial' in the older and more proper sense of that which is made by skill and artifice. Thus used, it is certainly not a derogatory term.

[2] Ch. XVI.

some other course, is a matter of historical research. This has been neglected by historians in the past because it has been supposed that physics is in some way 'natural,' and that in consequence there could be only one physics, which physicists over the centuries have been slowly unfolding. But the point of view advocated here shows that there could be an indefinite number of physics. Why did the Renaissance physicists launch physics off in the particular direction in which they did in fact launch it? The historians of physics have as yet scarcely broken the surface of this subject because of their adherence to the realist theory of physics.[1]

Undoubtedly the metaphysical schools of the 14th and 15th centuries had considerable psychological influence on the new physicists of the 16th and 17th centuries. The direction taken by modern physics will be better understood when later medieval philosophy is rescued from its present oblivion.

*Physics and Nature*

The world of modern physics is not the natural world. It is a remote domain of artifacts more removed from the world of Nature than the worlds in which Mr Pickwick and Hamlet dwell. The world of physics is austere and exacting, but withal a world of deep and abiding beauty. It is this aesthetic quality, perhaps even more than the satisfaction of intellectual curiosity and the desire for power, which explains its hold on its exponents. The beauty of pure mathematics has been recognised at least since the days of Plato. Pure physics has this beauty too, and in addition an intangible quality peculiar to itself which is well known to those who have entered its inner temples. This, rather than the exploration of Nature, must be the physicist's apology.

---

[1] Physics of course, has not, historically, been entirely univocal. We have already drawn attention to the existence of national divergences in physics (p. 26), and given as an example the inverse square law of force between electric charges *v*. Faraday's lines of force. Other examples could be given, e.g. Newton's 'force' *v*. Huyghen's 'potential energy' in elementary mechanics. Such divergences as these have not, however, intruded themselves very conspicuously. Physics has been moderately univocal.

But it may well be asked now : what is the relation between physics and Nature ? If physics dwells apart, how does it come into contact with Nature ? And furthermore, it may be asked, why is it so successful ?

In a general way, the solution of the first part of the question lies in the fact that the process of systematic experiment is selective and transforming. Hence it is that the transition is made from Nature to the abstract world, and *vice versa*. This is the link between the two worlds.

As regards the second question—why, if physics is an abstract and arbitrary system, is it so successful ?—we might ask in return, what is the standard of success ? How much more or less successful physics might have been had it been developed in different ways from the way it was in fact developed, we do not know. If the net dragged through the world by the physicists had been quite different, the outcome might have been very different too. It may have been much more successful, or much less so. We have no standard of comparison for success, so the question is scarcely profitable.

In discussing success it may be helpful to compare together two different branches of physics. The classical mechanics as applied to the solar system was generally regarded as a dazzling success. But at the other end of the scale the theory of electromagnetics is regarded today by most students of the subject as being in a state of well-nigh hopeless confusion, although with experience it can be made to work moderately well. Evidently some wrong turning was made early in the development of this latter branch of physics, and with the root trouble, whatever it is, firmly entrenched, the subject appears to be growing in disorder and chaos rather than improving. Evidently it would be better to start afresh from the beginning and drag some quite different net through the world in this particular realm.

Such considerations as these should give us pause before we speak lightly of the 'success' of physical science.

A variant on this question  Why if arbitrary then success ? is to insist that if a law or theory enjoys success, then, in the same measure, it is probable that Nature is really like the situation envisaged by that law or theory. E.g. if the law of Gravitation is well established in physics, then there must really be this Gravitation in the world, and so on. In answer to this objection we cannot do better than quote the words of Wittgenstein in his *Tractatus Logico-Philosophicus*, where he propounds much the same doctrine concerning the laws of physics as we have in this chapter. In the course of a most penetrating discussion of the subject he remarks :

The fact that it can be described by Newtonian mechanics asserts nothing about the world ; but *this* asserts something, namely, that it can be described in that particular way in which as a matter of fact it is described. The fact, too, that it can be described more simply by one system of mechanics than by another says something about the world.[1]

If the laws of physics were really found *in* the world, then the laws would tell us something about the world. But if the laws of physics are superimposed *on* the world, then the laws themselves tell us nothing about the world.[2] Only the character of the particular description which we effect in terms of the super-imposed law has any bearing on the world. It is only in this second order manner that we make contact with the world.[3]

*Hence there is no foundation for the assertion that in modern physics a law or theory, if successful, tells us what Nature is like.*

This is a most important conclusion.

## The Practice of Physics

Apart from the possibility of a far-reaching hyper-physics being developed, these new views about physics are not likely to make much direct difference to the *practice* of physics. But indirectly they may have a considerable effect. The delusion that modern physics is directly concerned with Nature, with space, time, matter, and so on, has undoubtedly hampered

---

[1] *Tractatus*, 6.342.

[2] This incidentally provides the solution to the controversy which raged throughout the Middle Ages concerning the status of the various systems of astronomy. See Appendix.

[3] See further pp. 97 f.

the growth of the science considerably during the last few centuries. The physicist should now become bolder when he realises that he, not Nature, is at the helm. He should more easily be able to cast aside old ties and inhibitions. Difficulties of a common sense and philosophical nature are frequently encountered in the acceptance of fundamentally new principles of physics, as e.g. on the introduction of relativity and quantum theories. These difficulties should not be experienced henceforth when it is realised that, in spite of misleading terms, the physical principles are *not* about the real world which we know so well. The physicist should become more conscious of the power he possesses to mould his subject when he is fully aware of his autonomy.

However, apart from this increased freedom, practice is not going to be altered one whit. The physicist spends most of his time applying the discipline he has so laboriously acquired. For this there is little need to know much about the whys and wherefores of the discipline. The main thing is to be able to use it. It makes little difference to the practice whether the laws of physics are *a priori* or not. In fact we usually find that the best experimental physicists are quite poor at discussing the nature of their subject. This is an observation which applies not only to physics, but is almost as true in literature, music, and art. The poet, the musician, and the painter, are often the last people to go to for an intelligible account of the foundation of their arts. They have a divine talent, they live the life. That is enough. It is for others, with aesthetic sensibilities, but of a more philosophical turn of mind, to enquire into the nature of the arts.

Returning to the physicist : in his laboratory, with his white coat on so to speak, it is scarcely exaggerating to say that he has some of the attributes of a robot and some of a slave. And quite rightly so. This is his function, and if he considers physics worth while the physicist must be prepared to subject himself to his stern taskmaster. He has a task to perform, and the best physicist is he who performs it most diligently.

This applies to by far the greater part of the average

physicist's working life. But occasionally he is called upon to promulgate a new theory or law. In its formulation he needs to exercise his imagination, and theoretical physicists in particular often combine an imaginative gift of a high order with their more ordinary capacity for routine discipline. This imaginative power has come particularly to the fore in recent times. Dirac's amazing theory of the positive electron is a good example.[1] With the wider spread of the Procrustean interpretation of physics, and the consequent increased emancipation of the subject, we may expect this imaginative element in physics to flower even more luxuriantly.

The whole question of the physicist's imaginative powers, and hence of the origin of the forms of laws and theories, is one which has been all too little discussed in histories of physics.[2]

## The Rôle of Physics

The new orientation to the subject is significant as regards the status of physics in the world. It is likely to make a considerable difference in the rôle of physics in man's thinking, whether he believes physics is wresting out the secrets of Nature, or whether he believes the whole thing is quite artificial, and only of utilitarian and aesthetic significance, valuable as these latter may be.

When it is generally realised that modern physics is not really telling us anything of the world about us, in other words that the ontological status of the world of physics is very low, then we might expect that physics will be allotted to its proper place as an auxiliary to life and a fascinating intellectual exercise.

[1] Very briefly, according to Dirac the whole universe is filled with a continuum of electrons of negative energy, i.e. of negative mass. A γ-ray quantum, of energy greater than one million electron-volts, may impart its energy to one of these electrons. The electron leaves the continuum, acquires positive mass, and is observed as an ordinary negatively charged electron. At the same time the quantum disappears, and the hole left in the continuum is the positive electron.

This phenomenon of the production of positive and negative electron pairs by the annihilation of a quantum may be observed in the Wilson Cloud Chamber.

After a short lapse of time the positive electron will meet a negative electron. The negative electron will fall into the hole, which is what the positive electron consists of. In this way both electrons are annihilated and the energy re-appears as a one million-volt quantum.

[2] See Ch. XI on Scientific Method.

Then, being released from our self-imposed shackles, we will be free to turn our attention elsewhere in search of the real world. There we will find real matter, time, and space. We learn more about time from the simple words of the hymn :

> Time, like an ever-rolling stream,
> Bears all its sons away.

than from any text-book of physics.

This mental freedom will be good for the layman, and it will be good, too, for the physicist, in so far as he is a man. For the physicist is not always in his laboratory disciplining himself. Sometimes he emerges into the real world of everyday life with its warmth and colour, hopes and fears, its beauty, love, laughter, tears, its good and its evil. This is a world of values, quite different from the monotone of physics where values have been systematically excluded. In this real world the physicist finds modern physics but a broken reed. Of course, no human being is completely devoid of the knowledge of real life. The complete and utter physicist could not continue to live. The physicist—like nearly all scientists—must lead something of a dual existence. He leads one life in the laboratory and another and quite different life outside it.

Finally, we must allude to a subject which will be discussed more fully in another chapter.[1] With the change in the status of physics we may expect a change in the prevailing fashions in contemporary schools of philosophy. Some of the most influential of these schools are ultra-empirical and positivistic in tone. The model for their thinking is, by and large, physics. They try to map out the world along lines appropriate to physics. For everything other than physics the result is incredible barrenness.

Now that we see physics in a different light, perhaps the philosophical craze to ape the physicist will die out, and philosophy can resume its proper rôle of comprehending the real world in so far as that is possible to us. Metaphysics has been held up to scorn and ridicule by many since the rise

[1] Ch. **X.**

of modern physical science. But now we see that physics does not deal with the real world at all. This is the province of metaphysics.

To scorn metaphysics in the name of modern physics is to misunderstand the situation. Metaphysics should thus come back into its own again, once physics has been relegated to its proper place.

## The Non-Physical Sciences

The Procrustean structure in science has reached a very high development in modern physics. What now of the other branches of modern science?

No more than the merest outline of an answer to that question can be given here.

When we examine the various branches of science we find them partly Procrustean, and partly descriptive, in varying proportions. In a science like Chemistry the Procrustean element appears to be large, while in a science such as Zoology it is quite small. But even in the most simply descriptive sciences it is not entirely absent. To what extent, e.g. is the division of the plant kingdom into rigid genera and species real, and to what extent is it Procrustean? Or, again, the division of the geological strata into discrete ages? It must be left to an expert examination to decide.

On the whole, however, it is no doubt true to say that biological, geological, and other such sciences are substantially descriptive and real, and in fact 'Aristotelean,' while as we move away towards modern physics we enter more and more Procrustean, and consequently autonomous and 'non-Aristotelean' realms.

Other pursuits, such as psychology, which may be dignified as sciences, will be discussed elsewhere.[1]

To anticipate a later chapter on Immanuel Kant, we may say, in the language of Kant, that in sciences of a more simply descriptive type we are like a pupil who listens to everything

[1] See Ch. XV on Systems of Psychology.

the teacher chooses to say, while in sciences which are more exact and Procrustean, we are like a judge who compels the witnesses to answer questions which he himself has formulated.

## Addendum : on Truth and Sophistry

Again to anticipate later chapters, we should make it clear that in upholding the theory of physics of such a writer as Eddington, we are *not* necessarily subscribing to any philosophical superstructure which Eddington himself may hold over and above his theory of physics.[1] Eddington may propound a mystical pantheistic idealism. In this he may be right or wrong (we believe wrong), but this does not in any way invalidate his Procrustean theory of physics, which is based on domestic considerations of physics itself.

Eddington in his *philosophy* belongs to what we shall describe later as the school of ' unifiers,' a school which we will have occasion to criticize somewhat adversely. But his interpretation of the nature of modern physics is, we maintain, soundly based.

[1] cf. our evaluation of Kant (Ch. VI).

# CHAPTER IV

# THE SIGNIFICANCE OF PROCRUSTEAN SCIENCE

*Of myself I say nothing : but in behalf of the business which is in hand I entreat men to believe that it is not an opinion to be held, but a work to be done ; and to be well assured that I am labouring to lay the foundation, not of any sect or doctrine, but of human utility and power. Next, I ask them to deal fairly by their own interests, and laying aside all emulations and prejudices in favour of this or that opinion, to join in consultation for the common good ; and being now freed and guarded by the securities and helps which I offer from the errors and impediments of the way to come forward themselves and take part in that which remains to be done. Moreover, to be of good hope, nor to imagine that this Instauration of mine is a thing infinite and beyond the power of man, when it is in fact the true end and termination of infinite error.*

> Francis Bacon : *Novum Organum.* (Quoted by Kant as a Motto to the 2nd Edition of his *Critique of Pure Reason*).

## The Name

IN the last chapter we examined modern physics and found it to be Procrustean in structure. This puts it in the categorial order. It partakes not of *physis* but of *nomos*. It is an autonomous creation with a pragmatic sanction.

Prior to Galileo, physics had been concerned with the *physis*. The laws then were read *in* Nature. (Or at least they were intended to be). But, after Galileo, increasingly arbitrary laws were read *into* Nature. In the modern world man has re-created Nature after his own fashion, his ultimate aim being power and control over his creation.

Thus while the ancient and medieval science is properly
named 'physics,' the post-Renaissance science is misnamed
when referred to as 'physics.'   For it does not pertain to the
*physis* but to the *nomos*.   Hence a more appropriate term for
modern so-called ' physics ' would be ' nomics,' and those who
practice it presumably ' nomicists.'   To go on calling the
science ' physics ' is disguising its proper nature and per-
petuating a confusion.   However, in deference to popular
usage, we shall retain the term 'physics' here where no
confusion is likely to arise.

## The Quest for Utility and Power

It was in the Renaissance and immediately succeeding times
that modern autonomous physics, or more properly 'nomics,'
emerged into the light of day. It came forward tentatively at
first but with more and more vigour as time went on.

Can we find historical reasons why this new science was born
at that particular time in the world's history?   This is a difficult
question, but perhaps we can put forward a few suggestions
which may throw some light on the matter.

Speaking in a general way we can say that with the
Renaissance there came a growth in ' worldliness ' and a
widespread decline in the vividness of the belief in immortality.
With this there came the emergence of the individual seeking
temporal power and glory.   In this way he sought some sort
of compensation for the lessened expectation of eternal life.
This aggrandisement of the individual and the   pursuit
of power is a marked feature of Renaissance history.   Men
tended to lose their relation of community and become
isolated social atoms.   Man in a way became his own God.
Politically this receives its expression in Hobbes' *Leviathan*,
where men are envisaged as appetitive warring atoms, and
society as built up artificially from these units by a social
contract.   This theme of man as a creature of desire has been
a powerful *motif* with political philosophers from that day to
this.   In a more general way we might say that post-
Renaissance man has tended to become introverted and

enclosed in the prison house of his own mind. The general solipsistic trend of modern philosophies is a reflection of this tendency to introversion.

With the breakdown of the feudal order came the emergence of the bourgeoisie with their quest for ever-expanding trade. Exploration and colonisation were pushed out all over the world. Expanding commerce, communications, war, industry, and so on, were making greater and greater demands that man should increase his mastery over Nature.[1]

Modern physics was conceived and nurtured as an instrument of power to answer this demand. This is a topic on which economic historians should be able to throw much light. But at the same time it must be remembered that the economic and utilitarian forces provide rather the *conditions* favouring and directing the growth of the new sciences and working quietly in the background. The pioneer modern physicists themselves would only rarely be aware at the conscious level of the economic promptings. Their principal psychological drive was undoubtedly in most cases more intellectual.

### Francis Bacon

One in whom the new forces did rise to the conscious level however, and achieved a very clear expression, was a man who was not himself a practising physicist, but rather an intelligent onlooker. As is so often the case, the onlooker sees most of the game. He was Francis Bacon, Lord Chancellor of England (1561–1626). In the voluminous writings of Bacon is to be found a most illuminating account of the new *Weltanschauung*.

Bacon drew up his vision of the future in the form of an allegory of the '*New Atlantis.*' In this realm there is found 'Salomon's House' which was to be the centre of the new dispensation. (This is a foreshadowing of the Royal Society which was founded in England some twenty years after Bacon's death). Bacon lays it down that the end of its foundation is :

[1] See *The Social and Economic Roots of Newton's Principia*, by Professor B. Hessen for a Marxist analysis.

the knowledge of causes, and secret motions of things ; and
the enlarging of the bounds of human empire, to the effecting of all
things possible.

Prominent among the workers in that House are :
three that bend themselves, looking into the experiments of their
fellows and cast about how to draw out of them things of use and
practice for man's life, and knowledge as well for works as for plain
demonstration of causes, means of natural divinations, and the easy
and clear discovery of the virtues and parts of bodies.

From this manifesto we can see how Bacon's thoughts were
turning towards the useful and the practical.[1]

No one, perhaps, has discussed the significance of the new
learning with more clarity than Lord Macaulay. In his
eloquent *Essay on Francis Bacon* he writes:

The chief peculiarity of Bacon's philosophy seems to us to have
been this, that it aimed at things altogether different from those
which his predecessors had proposed to themselves. This was his
own opinion. ' Up-to-date no one has satisfactorily proposed
what the end of knowledge is' says he. And again 'The most
serious mistake of all lies in deviating from the ultimate end of
learning.' And elsewhere he says ' So far as I know that end of
humanity has not been set out or defined in any way.' The more
carefully his works are examined, the more clearly, we think, it will
appear that this is the real clue to his whole system, and that *he
used means different from those used by other philosophers, because he
wished to arrive at an end altogether different from theirs.*

What then was the end which Bacon proposed to himself ? It
was, to use his own emphatic expression, 'fruit.' It was the
multiplying of human enjoyments and the mitigating of human
sufferings. It was ' the relief of man's estate.' It was ' To be
devoted to human enjoyments.' It was ' To be used effectively
for the mitigation of the discomforts of human life.' It was ' To
endow human life with new aids and resources.' It was ' straight-
way to endow the human race with new arts and capabilities."
This was the object of all his speculations in every department

---

[1] Francis Bacon was not the first whose inclinations were more towards doing
than knowing. His namesake Roger Bacon, in the 13th century, might be cited
as a kindred spirit. But the earlier movements did not flourish, and it was not
until the 17th century that such ideas really took root. The main stream of later
medieval thought was associated with the *philosophia perennis*, and was intellectual
rather than practical.

of science, in natural philosophy, in legislation, in politics, in morals.

Two words form the key of the Baconian doctrine, *Utility* and *Progress.* The ancient philosophy disdained to be useful and was content to be stationary. It dealt largely in theories of moral perfection, which were so sublime that they never could be more than theories ; in attempts to solve insoluble enigmas ; in exhortations to the attainment of unattainable frames of mind. It could not condescend to the humble office of ministering to the comfort of human beings. All the schools contemned that office as degrading ; some censured it as immoral . . . 'It is not the office of philosophy to teach men how to use their hands. The object of her lessons is to form the soul,' says Seneca.

And later :

Assuredly if the tree which Socrates planted and Plato watered is to be judged of by its flowers and leaves, it is the noblest of trees. But if we take the homely test of Bacon, if we judge of the tree by its fruits, our opinion of it may perhaps be less favourable. . . . . .

The ancient philosophers did not neglect natural science ; but they did not cultivate it for the purpose of increasing the power and ameliorating the condition of man. The taint of barrenness had spread from ethical to physical speculations. Seneca wrote largely on natural philosophy, and magnified the importance of that study. But why ? Not because it tended to assuage suffering, to multiply the conveniences of life, to extend the empire of man over the material world ; but solely because it tended to raise the mind above low cares, to separate it from the body, to exercise its subtlety in the solution of very obscure questions.

The new philosophy differed from the ancient, Macaulay goes on to say, not merely in method but also in object. Its object was the good of mankind, in the sense in which the mass of mankind always have understood and always will understand the word good.

Macaulay then proceeds to make an instructive comparison between Plato and Bacon.

While Macaulay, with his eminently practical turn of mind, under-estimates the deeper value of the ancient philosophy, and over-estimates the shallower advantages of the Baconian, there is no doubt that he correctly represents the general opinions of Bacon and his contemporaries.

*The New Method and the Old*

The 17th century world was seeking practical 'fruits.'
The traditional philosophy of the world reached towards
knowledge of the real nature of things, to the existence of God,
and the destiny of man. But the post-Renaissance era with
its 'worldliness,' and its fundamental Pelagianism,[1] wanted
something more immediately here and now. It was to answer
this demand that the modern sciences grew up, and in particular
modern physics. These sciences cared little for the ultimate
nature of things. They took a short cut, as it were, to seize
the fruits of this world. It was at this time that the spirit of
modern pragmatism was born. It was no longer: 'is this
really the case?' 'is it the truth?' but: 'does it work?'
'is it useful?' 'Anything will do if it succeeds.' Though
scarcely understood at the time, it was Procrustes and Protagoras who were called in to be the high priests of the new order.
Under their ministrations was brought about the slow transition
from the real to the categorial order, and Bacon's 'fruits'
were reaped in abundant harvest.

We may conclude this section with a brief quotation from
Fr. Clarke.[2] Referring to the new empirical ' Method of
Discovery ' he writes :

Of the physical sciences it is perfectly true that in medieval
times they did not make any very rapid progress. Since the
Reformation, physical science has advanced with giant strides.
Material civilization has been developed to an extent that would
have been scarcely possible if the Church had not lost her dominion
over a large part of modern Europe. Victories have been won over
Nature of which the Schoolmen never dreamed, and the spirit
of enterprise, unchecked by fear of authority, has fought its way
with astonishing success in all the natural arts and sciences.

But is the same true of the sciences that deal not with the material
but the immaterial ? Not with the visible but with the invisible ?
Not with brute matter but with mind, thought, conscience, God ?

[1] On the Pelagian heresy as the besetting sin of modern times, see Alban
Goodier : *History and Religion* (London, 1937).
[2] Clarke, R. F. : *Logic* (London, 1889), pp. 476 ff.

It is on the answer to this question that must depend our approval or disapproval of the Scholastic Method. . . .

If the new method has proved a failure when once the consideration of the corruptible things around us is exchanged for the study of the incorruptible and eternal, then we shall rejoice in the conservative maintenance of the *a priori* method by Scholastic Philosophers, even though they forfeited thereby the superior acquaintance with Heat and Light, with Physiology and Botany and Chemistry, which is the boast of the present day.

In these passages Fr. Clarke makes clear the distinction between the old and the new, and the different fields in which each excels. He does not make so clear, however, what will be examined in detail in later chapters, that *both these methods may coexist side by side without enmity*. The practice of the new method, as we shall see, is quite compatible with the maintenance of the old, provided the new method is confined to its proper sphere. It is when the principles of the new method are applied outside that sphere (as is often mistakenly done) that a serious collision occurs. This duality is by no means obvious *prima facie* and only a careful examination will establish it.

Granted the duality, there is no need to conclude that if the Church and its Philosophy had continued their universal reign the conquests over Nature would *never* have been won. But it is no doubt true that they would not have come so quickly. This, however, from the point of view of the Church, is a comparatively trifling matter, since practical fruits occupy but a lowly position in the hierarchy of Being.

## The 'Otherness' of Modern Physics

Post-Galilean physical science is cut off from the rest of the world and is the creation of man himself. Consequently the science, in itself, has no immediate metaphysical foundations, and no metaphysical implications, in spite of popular beliefs to the contrary. These beliefs arise from the failure to realise the science's 'otherness,' that it belongs to the categorial order and not to the real order.

Only that which belongs to the real order is directly linked with metaphysics. The ancient and medieval science of physics belongs to this real order, and is, in principle, an integral part of philosophy in general. It *has* metaphysical foundations and metaphysical implications.[1]

But the 'new science' shifted across by degrees into the categorial order and consequently severed its immediate link with metaphysics. Few people were aware of this,[2] least of all the physicists themselves. The general run of physicists and philosophers have gone on writing learned works on the metaphysical foundations, and more particularly the metaphysical implications, of modern physics, oblivious to this change of character. If the theory of the nature of modern physics put forward in this book is correct, then both these enquiries are vain.

Works on the supposed metaphysical foundations of modern physics may have some value however, even if not in the sense intended by the authors. For, although logically the supposed foundations are not there, yet psychologically the metaphysical background may well have prompted the physicist to introduce this or that category or Procrustean bed. It is *one* of the sources of inspiration[3]. Such enquiries then are of great interest to the historian of science as indicating one possible factor which led the physicists to do what they in fact did. But they do not in any way provide a metaphysical foundation for the science, since a categorial science has no such

[1] This is not to say that all the particular Aristotelean doctrines of the Earth, the Skies, the Heavens and so on, are essential to Aristotelean metaphysics. *They are integrated with metaphysics only in their general intention, and not in particular formulation.* They could be modified without necessitating any change in metaphysical principles since the principles of metaphysics are founded on more general grounds.

Many of the particular Aristotelean opinions about phenomena were abandoned in the 17th century with the increasingly detailed knowledge of Nature. Galileo's *Dialogues on the Two Great Systems of the World* is a classic account of this revision of detailed theories of phenomena. Galileo himself, unlike many of his more extravagant followers, generally pursued this revision with considerable moderation. (See Ch. XVII). He is careful to distinguish what is true and abiding in Aristotle from what is erroneous and non-essential.

[2] See Ch. XVII on the enlightened views of such men as Cardinal Bellarmine in the very early days of the movement. Unfortunately, Bellarmine's wise observations were forgotten in later years. See, too, Ch. VI on Immanuel Kant, who held the clue in the hollow of his hand, but by excess destroyed it.

[3] See Ch. XI on Scientific Method.

foundation, dwelling apart, as it does, from the real world.[1]

While discussions of the metaphysical foundations of modern physics are comparatively rare, discussions of its supposed implications are extremely popular. In fact the implications of science are the happy hunting grounds of generations of philosophers, and physicists turned amateur philosophers.

Anxious theologians scan the latest scientific theories to see if they do or do not support the existence of God. Grave scientists issue their pontifical pronouncements. Sir James Jeans tells us that God is a great mathematician ; Einstein says ' God is slick but not mean ' ; Laplace, answering Napoleon who taxed him with not mentioning God in his *Mécanique Céleste*, said : 'I have no need of that hypothesis.'

[1] Such a work is the valuable study of Burtt: *The Metaphysical Foundations of Modern Science* (London, 1925). We might say that the significance of this work is not logical, as Burtt apparently intended, but psychological and historical. It is significant that Burtt practically ignores Kant and his Copernican revolution, which is of vital importance in this matter and leads to quite different conclusions from Burtt's (see Ch. VI.)

Reference should be made to E. W. Strong : *Procedures and Metaphysics* (Univ. of California Press, 1936) for an examination of the origin of modern physics from the non-metaphysical point of view advocated in this work. Strong writes (pp. 10-11):

The operational autonomy of science and the irrelevance of the metaphysical tradition was a conclusion arising from, rather than being a premise leading to, the present study. The theory with which the inquiry began was not confirmed by the evidence, for let it be confessed at the outset that the original intention was to consolidate the claim that the Platonic tradition was the metaphysical godfather of modern scientific thought. The study of the scientific work and opinion of the early-modern period conjoined with a correlated study of the mathematical aspect of the Platonic tradition revealed that the original theory was untenable. The problems of mathematicians and physical investigators were found to be methodological rather than proceeding from, or based on, metaphysical concepts. The meaning of concepts employed by mathematicians and scientists in their work was found to be established in the limited operations and subject matter constituting the science. *The conclusion finally driven home was the conviction that the achievements of Galileo and his predecessors were in spite of rather than because of prior and contemporary metaphysical theories of mathematics.*

This contention that there are two lines of activity, one of autonomous procedures, and the other of metaphysics, is diametrically opposed to Burtt's thesis of homogeneity. Strong goes on to develop it with a wealth of historical evidence. Strong's conclusions from his examination of the origins of modern mathematical-physical science in the 16th and 17th centuries lend powerful support to our basic contention that there are two orders : an autonomous order of physico-mathematical science, and a real order which is the province of metaphysics. The contention as advanced here is founded on an examination of the nature of physical science as we have it today. Strong's historical examination of origins is complementary to, and confirmatory of, the present work.

Puzzled philosophers delve into the intricacies of the Heisenberg uncertainty principle to determine if man does or does not possess free will, or to see if the law of causality remains valid, or if it has to be replaced by statistical probability.[1]

Learned authors are professing to find contemporary physics confronted with great 'crises.' Almost every physicist with leisure on his hands is publishing works on what he believes are the philosophical implications of his science, or conversely trying to show that all philosophy is vain, that metaphysics is a chimera, and religion a fraud. Others again

---

[1] As representative of a multitude of contemporary philosophers, let us quote one of the most acute, John Wisdom :

In general philosophers concern themselves with paradoxes arising from facts that come under their observation. It is important that they should be alive to the paradoxes arising from quantum facts. Such facts cannot be shelved as merely technical or as belonging to a special department ; they are facts along with all the other more familiar facts about nature ; they are no less real because revealed by complicated laboratory apparatus than are those revealed by the human eye. (*Mind*, Jan. 1947, p. 81).

These remarks of Wisdom's are largely vitiated by the author's failure to take into account the Procrustean character of physics. He is tacitly assuming a realist theory or a *passive* phenomenalism (Ch. XVIII). See p. 65 for further doctrines of this author consequent upon his failure to distinguish two orders.

As an amusingly ironic account of the extravagances into which popular opinion is led by hypostatising the world of physics, let us quote from Aldous Huxley's *Time Must Have a Stop* (London, 1945), Ch. 8.

' As I was saying, Mr Barnack, everyone ought to know something of Einstein.'
' Even those who can't understand what he's talking about ? '
' But they *can*,' the other protested. ' It's only the mathematical techniques that are difficult. The principle is simple—and after all, it's the understanding of the principle that affects values and conduct.'

Eustace laughed aloud.

' I can just see my mother-in-law changing her values and conduct to fit the principles of relativity ! '

' Well of course she *is* rather elderly,' the other admitted. ' I was thinking more of people who are young enough to be flexible. For example, that lady who acts as Mrs Gamble's companion. . . .'

' . . . Mathematically speaking, almost illiterate ' the young man was saying. ' But that doesn't prevent her from realizing the scope and significance of the Einsteinian revolution.'

' And what a revolution,' he went on with mounting enthusiasm. ' Incomparably more important than anything that had happened in Russia or Italy. For this was the revolution that had changed the whole course of scientific thinking, brought back idealism, integrated mind into the fabric of Nature, put an end for ever to the Victorians' nightmare universe of infinitesimal billiard balls.'

' Too bad,' said Eustace in parenthesis. ' I really loved those little billiard balls.'

call on their science to support some social or political scheme
to which they happen to adhere.

On examining the works of these scientific writers we
generally detect them purporting to find evidence from their
science for whatever they happen to believe *on other grounds*.
Their extra-scientific opinions are, unfortunately, for the most
part merely the casual opinions and prejudices of daily life.
For, in spite of the great prestige which the modern scientist
commands, it should be remembered that the rigours of his
professional studies will in most cases have prevented him
from gaining an adequate acquaintance with, and mastery
over, the no less rigorous fields of metaphysics, theology, politics,
morals, etc. His acquaintance with these topics is only too
often merely casual, and his well-meaning efforts to support
some cause dear to his heart by means of his science are usually
quite uncritical and naïve.

The scientist rightly commands respect, *in his own field.*
But outside that field he speaks only as a man, and his opinions
and arguments are as those of other men, and should be treated
accordingly with due reserve. It is a pernicious error of our
times to give undue weight to the opinions of scientific men
outside their own sciences.

The categorial theory of modern physics silences this babel
of voices immediately, for if modern physics is categorial
then it is not subject to metaphysics. It dwells in a world
of its own and enjoys autonomy therein. Conversely attempts
to deduce metaphysical consequences from the science, i.e.
assertions about the nature of the real world, are illusory.
Modern physics can in reality tell us nothing about God, about
free will, about causation, etc.[1] The illusion that it can do so

---

[1] Following on our previous footnote on p. 54, n. 1, it should be noted that while
modern physics contributes nothing to genuinely metaphysical matters, yet it
may have something to say on matters which were once closely linked, in
principle, with metaphysical enquiries, although not essential to them. E.g.
the doctrine held by Aristotle and his successors that heavenly bodies are composed
of a special element different from anything on Earth. The spectroscope, while it
can give us no knowledge of the real nature of things, does suggest however
that the elements of which the stars are composed are not substantially different
from those on Earth.

springs from the belief that it still pertains to the real world, like its predecessor, ancient physics. This belief in turn is encouraged by the continued use of terms belonging to the real order : terms like matter, force, cause, etc., which disguise the transition from the real to the categorial order.

Consequently there is no need for theologians to concern themselves unduly about modern physics ; it has no bearing on natural theology. Furthermore the so-called ' crisis ' in contemporary physics is a sham, a storm in a teacup. Similarly philosophers will not find any solution to the free will-determinism problem in the theories of Heisenberg and Schrödinger, nor will they discover from the modern physicists whether Nature is atomic, or statistical, or uncertain, or of any other constitution.[1]

## Modern Physics and Ethics

But if modern physics has left the real order behind it, it is becoming an ever more powerful practical tool for manipulating the world about us. Bacon's tree is certainly bearing fruits. This means that the significance of physics has passed from the realm of metaphysics to that of ethics. In its new home it is both the hope and despair of moralists. Bacon's rosy optimism of the beneficial effect on mankind of the ' fruits ' of the new science has been balanced, and perhaps more than balanced, by its evil fruits. The proper use of modern science as a practical tool has become one of the most urgent questions of our times, particularly, as a modern writer sees it, in view of the ' plain fact that the gigantic increase since about 1600 in man's power to control nature had not been accompanied by a

---

[1] The principle of indeterminacy is commonly held to be a new and fundamental departure from the principles of classical physics. This is quite an error. Indeterminacy is at least as old as the kinetic theory of gases, according to which the pressure of a gas is a statistical average due to the bombardment of the sides of the vessel by the particles composing the gas. With the kinetic theory of gases determinism was removed from the macroscopic world and transferred to the elementary particles. Now, with the theories of Heisenberg and Schrödinger, determinacy has been withdrawn from the elementary particles and transferred to the mathematical equations.

The Heisenberg principle of indeterminacy is not a new principle, but a change in the point of application of a long-standing principle in physical science.

corresponding increase, or anything like it, in his power to control human situations.'[1]

Connected with this matter of science and ethics is a common misconception. It is sometimes supposed that the modern experimental sciences, including modern physical science, have some contribution to make to the *principles* of morals. But this belief is unfounded. Modern physics has no bearing whatever on moral principles. Its moral significance lies entirely in the practical realm.

---

[1] Collingwood, R. G. : *Autobiography* (Oxford, 1939) Ch. 9. Cf. Breasted's remarks in his *Dawn of Conscience* (London, 1934) p. ix :

As the oldest known implement-making creature man has been fashioning destructive weapons for possibly a million years, whereas conscience emerged as a social force less than five thousand years ago. One development has far outrun the other ; because one is old, while the other has hardly begun and still has infinite possibilities before it.

The two authors differ on the location of the defect. Breasted believes that conscience is as yet inadequately developed. Collingwood believes conscience to be adequate, but the power to control human situations to be inadequate. Both agree in attributing the acuteness of the present situation to the rise of the manipulative sciences whereby we control Nature.

# CHAPTER V

# FROM *PHYSIS* TO *NOMOS*

*Which fairy tale serves best to remind us of the clusters of phenomena in nature?*

JOHN WISDOM.

*'But we must turn our eyes yonder, Glaucon.'*
*'Whither?'* he asked.
*'To the soul's love of wisdom, and observe what she apprehends, and after what company she strives, led on by her kinship to the divine and immortal and that which ever is.'*

*. . . Before, he had been seeing mere foolish phantoms, while now he is nearer to being, and is turned to what in a higher degree is, and is looking more directly at it.*

PLATO.

## Physis and Nomos

WE have seen how the science of physics in the 17th century made the transition from *physis* to *nomos*, from the real order to the categorial order. And yet much which properly pertains to the real order is retained in the categorial physics, but now only in outward form. In the past a good deal of the inspiration in categorial physics has come from metaphysics, in that metaphysics has often *suggested* fertile ideas. But the criterion, of course, is not that the ideas have or have not a metaphysical sanction, but that they measure up to the test of empirical success.

As one instance, in a teeming multitude of instances, let us consider arguments about action at a distance. These arguments might be described as 'metaphysical,' and yet according to the side on which the physicist ranged himself, so the course of his physics was directed. Those who upheld action at a distance on general grounds tended, in the electromagnetic theory, to formulate such laws as Coulomb's inverse square law of force between electric charges. These are pure action at a distance laws. At the same time others, such as Faraday, who were repelled by the idea of action at a distance, thought more in terms of the action of the intervening medium, of fields and lines of force. Such suggestions as these direct the form of the Procrustean beds to be used by the physicists. The metaphysical background is psychological rather than logical.[1] It is *one* of many sources of suggestions for the physicist when he is casting around looking for a suitable Procrustean bed.[2]

## The Atomic Theory

With these considerations in mind we can go on to a revealing example of the transition from *physis* to *nomos* : the atomic theory.

The ancient atomic theory of Leukippos and Demokritos was pre-eminently a metaphysical theory. It pertained to the real constitution of the world. Aristotle, discussing how it is possible for action and passion to take place, writes :

The most systematic and consistent theory, however, and one that applied to all bodies, was advanced by Leukippos and Demokritos.[3]

Aristotle goes on to discuss what is clearly the derivation of atomism from Eleatic metaphysics. Burnet's interpretation[4] is that Leukippos effected a plurality of the Parmenidean ONE. Each atom was, as it were, a Parmenidean sphere in miniature. The theory of Leukippos was, Burnet holds, the

---

[1] For an interesting discussion of notions of action at a distance, and their effect on physical theories, see Clerk Maxwell, J. : *Scientific Papers*, v. 2, p. 311, ' On Action at a Distance.' Also Clerk Maxwell : *A Treatise on Electricity and Magnetism* v. 2, §§ 865–6. This discussion is a good illustration of the complex interaction between metaphysics and physics in the minds of physicists. We allow the metaphysical background only a psychological status in modern categorial physics.

[2] This matter is discussed further in Ch. XI, on Scientific Method.

[3] *De Generatione et Corruptione*, 324$^b$ and 325$^a$.

[4] Burnet, John : *Early Greek Philosophy* (Edinburgh, 1892). Ch. IX.

final answer of the earlier Greek philosophers to the question of Thales: 'What is the *physis* of all things?', the question with which Greek philosophy started its career.

Whatever may have been its precise origin, it is clear that *the ancient atomic theory was the product of pure reason. It was a theory of the real. It pertained to 'physis,' not to 'nomos.'*

The atomic theory went through many vicissitudes during the next two thousand years or so. But in the early years of the 19th century it was revived and brought to the forefront of science by the Manchester chemist, John Dalton. He borrowed the ancient theory of atoms to account for the empirically determined chemical laws of definite, multiple, and equivalent proportions.

This new atomic theory, however, unlike its ancient predecessor, was not in any way metaphysical. *The new atomic theory was not a theory of the ultimate nature of things, of the real. It was merely a device to account for the chemical laws.* Indeed, it can hardly be said even to 'account' for the laws. For there was no more in the theory of atoms in the hands of John Dalton than in the data from which it was derived. It therefore, in fact, explained nothing, but it was valuable nevertheless as a mnemonic. For it co-ordinated and held together a number of different factors. It served as a sort of shorthand way of saying a lot in a little. As the years went by it grew stronger and stronger. Its great success towards the middle of the 19th century in the kinetic theory of gases and the dynamical theory of heat put it on a firm basis. For this was support from quite a different field to that in which it had been conceived, showing it to be fruitful.

By the end of the 19th century, the atom was no longer held to be indivisible, and interest began to be transferred from the atom itself to its constituent particles. With the Rutherford-Bohr theory, the atom, as such, became just a little indefinite, since now it was pictured as a sort of miniature solar system, which is not such a precise entity as the older concept of a hard indivisible elastic sphere. The elementary particles in this system are the electron, the proton, the neutron, and more recently the meson, the neutrino, and so on. And dwelling somewhat apart are the quanta.

In the last twenty years, however, since the days of Heisenberg and Schrödinger, with their theory of wave mechanics, even these elementary sub-atomic particles have become more and more nebulous. For now the centre of interest is the quantity $\psi$. In a sense we could say that the world of physics nowadays is made up basically not of 'matter,' nor of particles, but of $\psi$. This might seem paradoxical, but actually $\psi$ now performs much the same function as 'matter' and particles once performed, only it performs it more successfully. It is true that in wave mechanics there is still much *discourse* about particles and waves. But the impression grows that such discourse could be eliminated if necessary. It is not essential, but it is convenient for purely practical purposes of organizing the material of the subject. *Particles have now become little more than mnemonics to simplify discussions of $\psi$.*

As an instance of how particles have become more and more nebulous, we might mention that, according to one way of interpreting the Schrödinger equation, we are obliged to say that every electron fills the whole universe, only that it is much more 'concentrated' in the immediate vicinity of one point than any other. Alternatively we can refrain from saying that the electron exists anywhere, but hold that there is a certain ascertainable probability of its being observed at any given point in the universe. It is quite clear that with such a theory it is scarcely possible to speak literally of 'particles,' and as for atoms, they can be retained in the discourse only by courtesy.[1]

This will suffice as a sketch of the career of the atomic theory in modern science.

The elementary particle theory in modern physics is a Procrustean bed which can be taken up or dropped at will.[2] It is not a theory of the real nature of things. It is not a

---

[1] Nevertheless of course it is quite right for the chemist still to speak of atoms in ordinary chemistry, since there they play practically the same rôle as ever.
[2] cf. Ch. III.

metaphysical or ontological theory. It belongs not to the real order, but to the categorial.

*There are thus two atomic theories* : the ancient and the modern. The one *physis* and the other *nomos*. One of the real and metaphysical, the other categorial and of the character of a mnemonic, the atoms being mental artifacts.

## The Evidence and the Evidenced

Whether Leukippos and Demokritos be right or wrong in their metaphysical theory does not particularly concern us here. (Scholastic philosophers of course hold that the ultimate constitution of bodies is *not* accounted for by atomism but, following Aristotle, by the twofold principle of prime matter and substantial form.[1])

The point we are concerned with is that the ancient atomic theory, being metaphysical, holds that there really are atoms lying behind the phenomenal world about us, and in which the phenomena have their roots so to speak. Here is the *evidence*, and there is the *evidenced* ; they are separate and distinct.

The modern scientific theory, on the other hand, employs atoms merely as convenient mnemonics to organise the data. The atoms in the scientific theory do not enjoy any separate, real, ontological status. *The evidenced, the atoms, is, in a sense, no more than the evidence.*[2]

These considerations give a clue to the popular contemporary discussions on such topics as ' Are there such things as minds ?' The neo-positivists who maintain that a ' mind ' is simply a mnemonic, an artifice, to co-ordinate the category of what

[1] See Ch. XIX.

[2] This statement, though convenient for brevity, may be misleading. For there may be many other mental artifices which would act as mnemonics for the same subject matter. And furthermore, and more important in modern physical science, there is not just ' the evidence ' since ' the evidence ' is arrived at after a great deal of selection and interpretation. This is part of the Procrustean transformation. E.g. an apparently stray mark on a photographic plate may mean nothing to the layman, but may have a wealth of meaning for the physicist, who sees in it the track of a charged particle. In other words the *data* of the physicists are not by any means to be identified with the *phenomena* of the empiricist philosophers.

we call mental events, are taking the same view as in modern scientific atomism. They maintain that the evidenced, the mind, is the same as the evidence. 'There is nothing more than events,' is the proposition maintained by the older positivists. But the new positivists add that we can conveniently speak of a ' mind ' as an aid to simplify discourse.[1]

Thus they retain the term without the substance, and thereby reduce things to an empty shell. They can now speak with something of the language of the *philosophia perennis*, but it is in reality a sham.

These neo-positivists tend to model themselves on modern scientific theories. This can be well seen in the very interesting series of articles in *Mind*, by John Wisdom, entitled : '*Other Minds*,' particularly the first of the series (*Mind*, 1940). He takes a number of selected examples and discusses them as we have done the modern theory of atoms, and having arrived at the same conclusion as we did, that they are of the class of mnemonics, he proceeds to use this as a model for his philosophy in general.

Had John Wisdom reflected, as we have done, that there are two atomic theories, the one metaphysical, the other serving the function of a mnemonic, and in fact that there are in general two orders, then he might not have been so hasty in generalising the mnemonic model into a basis for philosophy. The Cambridge neo-positivists, by failing to distinguish between real and categorial orders, and instead virtually treating everything as of the categorial order, have returned to the condition of some of the Sophists, notably Protagoras, only in a much more sophisticated way.

The modern 'Cambridge' school is subtle and elusive, but the summary by a recent author is probably not very far from the mark :[2]

The Wittgensteinian method of dealing with philosophical problems does not consist in offering a systematic theory about this or that feature of the world or about the world as a whole. . . .

[1] We shall see later how Ernst Mach is the father of this school of thought. (Ch. XVIII).
[2] Farrell, B. A. : *Mind*, 1946, p. 31.

*A and B* (two philosophical disputants) *must be shown that there is no one best insight or true answer ; that neither of them has a superior or better insight than the other.*

In this school of thought metaphysics is not explicitly rejected, but it tends to be regarded as a sort of persuasive poetry.

In general the mainspring of the school seems to be that the evidenced is just the evidence. Hence there is no point in disputing, e.g., whether the vagaries of my watch are due to an *invisible* brownie or an *invisible* leprechaun.[1] For the brownie and the leprechaun in this case are no more than the vagaries, or rather a mnemonic for the vagaries. The vagaries being agreed upon on all hands, further dispute can be merely verbal. We are inclined to say 'It's only a matter of which picture you paste on the back to remind you of the same peculiarities in the watch.'[2]

This is undoubtedly correct in so far as it is true that the brownie and the leprechaun cannot be reached in any other way than *via* the vagaries.

This of course is true by definition for our watch, and may even be true in general for brownies and leprechauns. The Irish, whose homeland is one where fairies are reputed to be indigenous, are best left to decide this latter point.

Another example is : 'the philosophical scientist who suddenly doubts whether a current runs in wires which gives off sparks, drives trains, etc.'[3] When he doubts if there is an invisible current in the wire, the scientist is not having any different expectations from anyone else. It is a very peculiar doubt, and we are tempted to say that *he isn't doubting anything*. He is like someone who suddenly says, 'Is there such a thing as a wind ? I see nothing except its effects (*sic*), the hurrying clouds, the flying leaves.'[4] This is a very *queer* doubt.

And again : 'In the same way, in a country where it is the custom to say of watches which sing fairy songs and disappear

[1] John Wisdom, *loc. cit.*, p. 379.
[2] *Ibid*, p. 384.
[3] *Ibid*, p. 384.
[4] *Ibid*, p. 390.

on Midsummer Night that they are haunted by invisible leprechauns, it is something of a joke to say " *Are* there any invisible leprechauns ? How do you know now that there is in this watch an invisible leprechaun ? " '

'To ask "Is there a current within ? " "Is there a leprechaun within or a brownie ? " is to ask which fairy tale we shall choose to remind us of the facts.'[1]

We can scarcely hope to do justice here to the subtlety and penetration of these articles of John Wisdom's, which are well nigh unique in modern philosophy. But we hope we have drawn attention fairly to the categorial plane on which these arguments move, and to the fact that they do not reach down to the real order.

## Atoms and the Evidence

Let us now sum up the situation regarding the atomic theory.

Can atoms be arrived at in any other way than *via* scientific data ? i.e. are they more than a mnemonic for that data ? The atoms of the modern scientific theory are arrived at solely *via* the data, and for them the evidenced is the evidence.[2] But the atoms of metaphysics, if they exist, belong to the real world and can be arrived at, if at all, by general philosophical reasoning. They are not of the class of John Wisdom's invisible brownies and leprechauns, and invisible currents. Their ontological status is much higher. In discussing philosophical atomism it is not in the least a matter of showing 'that there is no one best insight or true answer ; that neither disputant has a superior or better insight than the other.' For now we are no longer in the categorial, but in the real order, and here the considerations put forward by the Wittgensteinians are of no avail.

The failure of the Wittgensteinians to appreciate this springs from their neglect of the distinction between *physis* and *nomos*, and the complex interrelation between the two.

[1] *Ibid*, p. 402.
[2] See the qualification on p. 64, n. 2, to this common but over-simplified statement.

'*Isn't doubt without works dead?*' we might take as the main point of Wisdom's arguments. And very true it is indeed in certain fields. In fact Wisdom's gentle and yet forceful unfolding of this theme is one of the outstanding contributions to philosophy in recent times.

As far as the categorial order is concerned we may accept all that Wisdom has said. But we maintain that there is also a real or natural order with which metaphysics or ontology is concerned, and without which the categorial order itself would be meaningless. This real order is the field of the *philosophia perennis*. There the ground is not that contemplated by John Wisdom and the Wittgensteinian school. Whatever may be the case with other philosophies, the *philosophia perennis* is not built on mnemonics where doubt without works is dead : it is built on inescapable propositions, propositions which cannot be evaded, propositions which assert themselves in the very process of their attempted denial. This fundamental aspect of the world has been passed over at Cambridge.

The distinction between *physis* and *nomos* is then of the greatest importance. Its neglect leads to endless confusion in philosophy.

# CHAPTER VI

# IMMANUEL KANT

*This attempt to alter the procedure which has hitherto prevailed in metaphysics by completely revolutionising it in accordance with the example set by the geometers and physicists, forms indeed the main purpose of this critique of pure speculative reason.*

KANT : *Kritik,* B xxii.

*Thus the understanding is something more than a power of formulating rules through comparison of appearances ; it is itself the lawgiver of nature.*

KANT : *Kritik,* A 126

HAVING expounded the Procrustean character of modern physical science, let us now see what light it will shed on the interpretation of the philosophy of Kant.

## Kant's Starting Point

Immanuel Kant has suffered more than his fair share of obloquy at the hands of his opponents. Modern Scholastic philosophers are particularly prone to regard Kant as the arch-enemy. They certainly have some justification for this. Some of the most conspicuous parts of Kant's philosophical system : his theory of the categories, of phenomena and noumena, his criticism of the arguments for the existence of God, and so on, are alien to the *philosophia perennis.* Criticism of Kant is not difficult. He is a particularly vulnerable philosopher, and it is quite easy to demonstrate the formal falsity of many of his doctrines. But when this has been done it behoves us to go on and ask *why* Kany propounded these erroneous doctrines. Such an enquiry in the case of any philosopher is not without interest, and, in the case of Kant, it turns out to be most illuminating. Now it is just this enquiry which has been almost universally neglected by the critics of Kant, including the Scholastic critics.

This chapter might be regarded as a sort of prolegomena to Kant. In it we will try to repair the omission in Kantian scholarship and thereby do something towards rehabilitating a much under-estimated man. We will endeavour to make it clear why Kant said what he did. The system of Kant is not merely some unaccountable aberration. Kant really has something valuable to say to all philosophers, including the Scholastics. But he himself obscures this by the usual failing of philosophers : that of too wide a generalisation, of extending the truth he has seized upon out of its proper realm into regions where it does not hold. Indeed this well nigh universal habit of exaggeration is the key to understanding most of the philosophers who deviate in one way or another from the *philosophia perennis*.

Our task then is to rescue the truth which lies at the bottom of the Kantian philosophy. When we do so we shall find that it is indeed a truth worth rescuing. In fact, as we shall see, it carries in the germ the principle for which most modern Scholastics have long been searching in their endeavour to carry on the Thomist synthesis of knowledge by incorporating in the synthesis the autonomous post-Renaissance science.

Critics of Kant in the past have been mostly concerned to refute his system, or to investigate the minutiae of his doctrines, or to carry on learned discussions as to whether, and to what extent, Kant was an idealist or a realist, and so on. Little attention has been paid to fundamentals. *And the reason for this is that the Kantian foundations are not so much philosophical as scientific in origin.* The philosophical commentators have tended to fight shy of anything lying rather out of their field. The scientists on the other hand have been baffled by Kant's difficult philosophy, and have remained for the most part unacquainted with his scientific doctrines. Between the two there does not seem to have been much really fundamental enquiry into the springs of the Kantian philosophy.

Kant in his early life was primarily a physicist. He was keenly interested in mathematics, physics, and astronomy, as well as in philosophy. He was a student of Newton, and was well versed in all the latest scientific developments of his day. His early published works were mainly scientific. While still a student he published a work on Force. He wrote on such subjects as the retardation of the Earth's rotation on its axis, the age of the Earth, the relativity of motion, and the nature of the Atom. He published in 1755 a *General Natural History and Theory of the Heavens* in which he propounded the nebular hypothesis for the origin of the solar system, an hypothesis which was later to be put forward independently by Laplace, and is usually associated with the name of the latter.

Kant's early period then was one of considerable scientific activity. But it was not the activity of the pure scientist as such.[1] It was rather that of a critical and well informed mind reflecting on the scientific activity of his times. Kant was like an expert onlooker at a boxing match, able to appreciate all the finer points of the game. Such an onlooker is often in a much better position to understand what is going on than the boxers themselves, who, in the thick of the fight, are rarely operating at a fully self-conscious level. So with Kant. The detachment of the scholar of Königsberg enabled the new physical science to rise up to the conscious level in the mind of Kant. Kant saw more clearly than the scientists themselves what was going on. *What he detected in the new physical science was to become the crux of his whole attitude to the world.* He was imbued with his new discovery, and he spent the rest of his life writing philosophical works in which he expounded his great idea and developed and extended it into many avenues of human thought.

*It is his fundamental discovery about physical science which is Kant's really important contribution to thought. The philosophical system which he erected upon it may be rejected as a mere tour de force, and yet the primary discovery remains unshaken.*

[1] See e.g. Lindsay, A. D. : *Kant* (London, 1934), p. 24.

His general philosophy reaches its maturity in the *Critique of Pure Reason*, the first edition of which was published in 1781, and the second edition in 1787. In between the two editions he published his *Prolegomena* which contains a simplified version of the doctrine. The development of his theories in ethics and aesthetics, though dependent upon his fundamental thesis, need not detain us here.

Put briefly, *what Kant had detected in the new physical science was that the physicist is not passive but active. He does not passively recognise laws in Nature, he actively thrusts laws upon Nature.* This is the basis of Kant's philosophy. Kant alone realised this great principle. The general run of philosophers, particularly the English empiricists, and the physicists themselves, believed that we passively observed uniformities in Nature and generalised them into laws. Kant saw that the real state of affairs was quite different ; his doctrine amounted to a Copernican revolution in the theory of physical science.

Then he went a step further : *the activity of the physicist, Kant took as the activity of the human mind generally, and he developed his theory of physics into a general philosophy of the world.*

His primary doctrine concerning the true nature of modern physics seems to have been hardly appreciated by other philosophers. They have been mostly concerned with Kant's second step. In our own day the primary doctrine, in principle, has been re-discovered by such people as Poincaré and Eddington. This we have already discussed in some detail in Chapter III.

From the days of Kant until the present revival, a period of about 150 years, the theory of the categorial activity of the physicist lay dormant. It was buried beneath the enormous superstructure which Kant had erected upon it. Looking back now on Kant with the Procrustean bed theory of physics in mind, the system of Kant becomes much clearer. Propositions which tended to be obscure to commentators in the past now present few difficulties.

From our Procrustean standpoint we can see Kant in a new light. Kant was before his time. He was preaching to a world which only half understood the well-springs of his thought. But today we have caught up with Kant and we can appreciate his labours at more like their true value. We can appreciate the truth which lies within him, and we can appreciate, too, the unwarranted generalisations of which he was guilty.

To make Kant's fundamental discovery clearer, and to show how he built his philosophy upon it, and how unwarranted this latter step was, we will first of all consider the philosophical problem with which Kant was confronted and then the solution he proposed for it. Following that we will go on to discuss his solution in more detail.

## Kant's Problem

In the earlier part of his career Kant was a rationalist philosopher in the tradition of Leibnitz. But he was awakened from his dogmatic slumbers, as he tells us, by reading David Hume. Hume, as Kant understood him, had shown that metaphysics was a delusion. In particular, after a careful scrutiny of cause, Hume had decided that the causal connection between one thing and another could not be found in pure reason *a priori*, and he concluded that it was a habit of mind engendered by constant association in experience.

If we accept his conclusions, writes Kant, then all that we call metaphysics is a mere delusion whereby we fancy ourselves to have rational insight into what, in actual fact, is borrowed solely from experience, and under the influence of custom has taken the illusory semblance of necessity.[1]

Kant sums up the matter in the *Prolegomena*[2] :

The question was not whether the concept of cause was right, useful, and even indispensable with regard to our knowledge of nature, for this Hume had never doubted. But the question to which Hume expected an answer was this, whether that concept could be thought by the reason *a priori*, and whether it consequently possessed an inner truth, independent of all experience, and therefore applied more widely than to the mere objects of experience. It was surely a question concerning the *origin*, not concerning the *indispensable use* of the concept.

[1] *Kritik*, B 20. Kemp Smith's translation (London, 1929). (Following the precedent of Paton, we shall for brevity use *Kritik* to designate the *Critique of Pure Reason*).

[2] p. 5 (Mahaffy's translation, London, 1872).

Hume had concentrated on cause and effect. But after reflection Kant :

tried whether Hume's objection could not be put into a general form, and soon found that the concept of the connexion of cause and effect was by no means the only one by which the understanding thinks the connexion of things *a priori*, but rather that metaphysic consists altogether of such connexions.[1]

We might say here that Kant was finally to arrive at the conclusion that these concepts were not deduced by reason from experience, as Hume had rightly apprehended, nor did they come from custom, as Hume had vainly imagined, but in fact they sprang *a priori* from the pure understanding.

The general question with which Kant started was : is Hume right ? or is metaphysics at all possible ?

Kant felt that it was by no means obvious to begin with that there even was a science of metaphysics, since in all ages one metaphysician had contradicted another in assertions and proofs.[2]

To appreciate Kant's point of view it must be realised that for Kant metaphysical knowledge, if there be such, is not only *a priori* but also synthetic. Being synthetic means that the understanding has gone outside what is given in the subject and has actually acquired new knowledge, as e.g. in the proposition : 'the world was created in time.' Thus synthetic knowledge is opposed to analytic knowledge, which, Kant believed, is not anything new, but merely an explication of old knowledge E.g. 'bodies are extended' is analytic, since extension is part of our notion of body. But 'bodies are heavy' is synthetic since the attribute of heaviness is an extra attribute of bodies, i.e. is new knowledge.[3]

It is plain that all judgments of experience are synthetic since they extend our knowledge. But the problem is how can we have *a priori* synthetic judgments, since here the help of experience to effect the synthesis is lacking. Now upon what

[1] *Proleg.,* p. 7.
[2] *Proleg.*, pp. 20 f.
[3] *Kritik*, Intro. IV.

can we rely when we seek to go beyond the concept A and to know that another concept B is connected with it?

' What,' asks Kant, ' is here the unknown = x which gives support to the understanding when it believes that it can discover outside the concept A a predicate B foreign to this concept, which it yet at the same time considers to be connected with it? It cannot be experience, because the suggested principle has connected the second representation with the first, not only with greater universality, but also with the character of necessity, and therefore completely *a priori* and on the basis of mere concepts.'[1]

Thus the primary question: 'how is metaphysics possible?' becomes, so Kant thinks, the question: 'how is synthetic *a priori* knowledge possible?'

Kant admits that at first sight this problem seems insoluble[2] and that only experience can furnish connections, as Hume had said. *But, on the other hand, Kant believes that there already exist incontestable cases of synthetic a priori propositions, namely those of pure mathematics and physics.* It is Kant's belief that the propositions of mathematics and physics belong to this class, that impels him to go on with his enquiry. These are established and progressive sciences, so that if it is true that they employ synthetic *a priori* propositions, then the existence of such propositions in metaphysics does not seem so impossible after all. Hume, from this point of view, was unwittingly destroying pure mathematics when he denied in effect that there was *a priori* synthetic knowledge.[3]

Kant has not as yet solved the problem of *how* there can be *a priori* synthetic propositions, but he has no doubt that there *are* such propositions.

The question thus becomes: not merely how is metaphysics possible? but how is any sort of *a priori* synthetic knowledge possible? This will answer all cases of what we might call ' the general transcendental problem,' viz.:

How is pure mathematics possible?

How is pure physics possible?

How is metaphysics possible?[4]

[1] *Kritik*, B 13.    Kemp Smith's translation.
[2] *Proleg.*, p. 28.
[3] *Kritik*, B 20.
[4] *Kritik*, Intro. VI.

He goes on characteristically :

All metaphysicians are therefore solemnly and legally suspended from their occupations till they shall have answered in a satisfactory manner the question 'how are synthetic cognitions *a priori* possible ? ' [1]

He adds a qualification which is interesting in the light of modern linguistic philosophies, which tend to regard metaphysics as persuasive poetry :

If they, on the other hand, desire to carry on their business not as a *science* but as an *art* of persuasion, wholesome and suited to the general common sense of man, they cannot in justice be prevented.[2]

The primary question of the *Kritik* then is this :

'How are *a priori* synthetic judgments possible ? '

The problem, and the solution Kant proposes, is a challenge to all philosophers : 'You must adopt my solution, or thoroughly refute it and substitute another. To evade it is impossible,' he writes.[3]

### Kant's Theory of Mathematics and Physics

We have seen that what sustained Kant's belief in the existence of *a priori* synthetic propositions, in spite of the difficulty about *how* there could be such propositions, was his conviction that the propositions of the established sciences of mathematics and modern physics were of this type. He believed that neither mathematics nor physics had always been like this, but that with each science at a certain epoch a revolution had occurred which gave it this character. He placed the revolution in mathematics in the dim past among the ancient Greek philosophers. The revolution in physics he attributed to the labours of Galileo, Bacon, etc.

We will first quote Kant's own words on the subject as laid down in the Preface to the 2nd edition of the *Critique of Pure Reason*, and then follow his application of the new principle to metaphysics. Later we will go on to a critical examination of his theory of physics.[4]

[1] *Proleg.*, p. 29.
[2] *Proleg.*, p. 29.
[3] *Proleg.*, p. 11.
[4] p. 84.

Kant describes the revolutions in physics and mathematics thus :

When Galileo caused balls, the weights of which he had himself previously determined, to roll down an inclined plane; when Torricelli made the air carry a weight which he had calculated beforehand to be equal to that of a definite column of water ; or in more recent times, when Stahl changed metal into lime, and lime back into metal, by withdrawing something and then restoring it, a light broke upon all students of nature. They learned that *reason has insight only into that which it produces after a plan of its own,* and that it must not allow itself to be kept, as it were, in nature's leading-strings, but must itself show the way with principles of judgment based upon fixed laws, constraining nature to give answer to questions of reason's own determining. *Accidental observations, made in obedience to no previously thought-out plan, can never be made to yield a necessary law, which alone reason is concerned to discover.* Reason, holding in one hand its principles, according to which alone concordant appearances can be admitted as equivalent to laws, and in the other hand the experiment which it has devised in conformity with these principles, must approach nature in order to be taught by it. *It must not, however, do so in the character of a pupil who listens to everything that the teacher chooses to say, but of an appointed judge who compels the witnesses to answer questions which he has himself formulated.* Even physics, therefore, owes the beneficent revolution in its point of view entirely to the happy thought, that while reason must seek in nature, not fictitiously ascribe to it, whatever as not being knowable through reason's own resources has to be learnt, if learnt at all, only from nature, it must adopt as its guide, in so seeking, that which it has itself put into nature. It is thus that the study of nature has entered on the secure path of a science, after having for so many centuries been nothing but a process of merely random groping.[1]

Mathematics he believes had, long before, in the days of the Greeks, effected the revolution, and had thereby left the groping stage and entered upon the sure path of science[2]:

A new light flashed upon the mind of the first man (be he Thales or some other) who demonstrated the properties of the isosceles triangle. The true method, so he found, was not to inspect what

---

[1] *Kritik*, B xii ff. Kemp Smith's translation. Italics not in original.
[2] *Kritik*, B xi ff. Kemp Smith's translation.

he discerned either in the figure, or in the bare concept of it, and from this, as it were, to read off its properties ; but to bring out what was necessarily implied in the concepts that he had himself formed *a priori*, and had put into the figure in the construction by which he presented it to himself. If he is to know anything with *a priori* certainty he must not ascribe to the figure anything save what necessarily follows from what he has himself set into it in accordance with his concept.

This, then, in these general terms, is the revolution which Kant's study of the new physical sciences had led him to detect.

His doctrine as regards mathematics we will not pursue at present.[1] But as regards physics the theory announced here is one of the first importance. Its detection is Kant's great triumph. It is the one solid rock in his conception of the world, a rock which will not be worn away by criticism. Though all the rest of his philosophy be abandoned, this will remain.

### The Great Experiment : Metaphysics on the Paradigm of Physics

Kant now ventures out from the sure ground of physics to the troubled waters of metaphysics. Metaphysics, as he sees it, has hitherto been merely a random groping ; it has not yet entered upon the secure path of a science. It has, in the past, been a battle-ground for mock combats, but no real advance has ever been made. This is the gloomy picture to which Kant's rather narrow 18th century philosophical education had led him. Needless to say when we consider the stream of the *philosophia perennis* we see how really groundless are Kant's strictures on all metaphysics up to his time. But, remarkable as it may seem, the only acquaintance with the *philosophia perennis* which Kant seems to have had was with a shallow and degenerate form current in German Universities in his day. It was in this attenuated atmosphere that he came to despair of metaphysics.

[1] We shall see later (Ch. XII) that this theory of mathematics is relevant to non-Euclidean geometries, and to much of the modern structure of pure mathematics. It is *not* true however for Euclidean geometry and for operations with natural numbers.

Kant viewed the world through 18th century eyes with all its keenness of vision and yet all its narrowness.[1]

The plight of metaphysics, as Kant believed it to be, was, in his eyes, in great contrast to the flourishing state of mathematics and physics. He therefore conceived the idea of performing what he himself called tentatively *an experiment* : to carry out in metaphysics a revolution analogous to the revolutions which he believed had previously occurred in the two established sciences, and which had set them on the sure path. By this means he hoped to rescue metaphysics from the doldrums in which he supposed it to be languishing.

In the preface to the 2nd Edition he writes[2]:

' The examples of mathematics and natural science, which by a single and sudden revolution have become what they now are, seem to me sufficiently remarkable to suggest our considering what may have been the essential features in the changed point of view by which they have so greatly benefited. Their success should incline us, at least by way of experiment, to imitate their procedure, so far as the analogy which, as species of rational knowledge, they bear to metaphysics may permit.'

Then he goes on to make the Copernican revolution in metaphysics which is the turning point of the *Kritik*[3] :

Hitherto it has been assumed that all our knowledge must conform to objects. But all attempts to extend our knowledge of objects by establishing something in regard to them *a priori*, by means of concepts, have, on this assumption, ended in failure. We must therefore make trial whether we may not have more success in the tasks of metaphysics, if we suppose that objects must conform to our knowledge. This would agree better with what is desired, namely, that it should be possible to have knowledge of

[1] cf. Etienne Gilson : *The Unity of Philosophical Experience* (London, 1938), pp. 316-7. ' His (Kant's) condemnation of metaphysics was not the consequence of any personal attempt to reach the foundations of metaphysical knowledge. Kant busied himself with questions about metaphysics, but he had no metaphysical interests of his own. Even during the first part of his career there was always some book between this professor and reality. To him, nature was in the books of Newton, and metaphysics in the books of Wolff. . . . Before allowing Kant to frighten us away from metaphysics, we should remember that what he knew about it was mere hearsay.'

[2] *Kritik*, B xv f. Kemp Smith's translation.

[3] *Kritik*, B xvi f. Kemp Smith's translation.

objects *a priori*, determining something in regard to them prior to their being given. We should then be proceeding precisely on the lines of Copernicus' primary hypothesis. Failing of satisfactory progress in explaining the movements of the heavenly bodies on the supposition that they all revolved round the spectator, he tried whether he might not have better success if he made the spectator to revolve and the stars to remain at rest. A similar experiment can be tried in metaphysics, as regards the *intuition* of objects. If intuition must conform to the constitution of the objects, I do not see how we could know anything of the latter *a priori* ; but if the object (as object of the senses) must conform to the constitution of our faculty of intuition I have no difficulty in conceiving such a possibility. Since I cannot rest in these intuitions if they are to become known, but must relate them as representations to something as their object, and determine this latter through them, either I must assume that the *concepts*, by means of which I obtain this determination, conform to the object, or else I assume that the objects, or what is the same thing, that the *experience* in which alone, as given objects, they can be known, conform to the concepts. In the former case, I am again in the same perplexity as to how I can know anything *a priori* in regard to the objects. In the latter case the outlook is more hopeful. For experience is itself a species of knowledge which involves understanding ; and understanding has rules which I must pre-suppose as being in me prior to objects being given to me, and therefore as being *a priori*. They find expression in *a priori* concepts to which all objects of experience necessarily conform, and with which they must agree. As regards objects which are thought solely through reason, and indeed as necessary, but which can never—at least not in the manner in which reason thinks them—be given in experience, the attempts at thinking them (for they must admit of being thought) will furnish an excellent touchstone of what we are adopting as our new method of thought, namely, that we can know *a priori* of things only what we ourselves put into them.

The experiment of using the new physics as the model for metaphysics has succeeded. And in this way what Kant calls metaphysics in its first part, namely the part that is occupied with *a priori* concepts to which objects can be given in experience, has entered upon the secure path of a science. For now we see how there can be knowledge *a priori*.

*The Great Experiment : Its Result*

Kant has modelled metaphysics on the new physics. This allows us to have knowledge *a priori*. But another conclusion follows which has far reaching consequences. Let us quote Kant again :

This deduction of our power of knowing *a priori*, in the first part of metaphysics, has a consequence which is startling, and which has the appearance of being highly prejudicial to the whole purpose of metaphysics, as dealt with in the second part. For we are brought to the conclusion that we can never transcend the limits of possible experience, though that is precisely what this science is concerned above all else to achieve.[1]

This is Kant's fundamental denial of the possibility of metaphysics as ordinarily understood. We must distinguish between the appearances and the thing in itself. Our *a priori* knowledge has only to do with appearances. The thing in itself is real but cannot be known by us. The thing in itself is always beyond our knowledge and inaccessible, since it is always subject to, and behind the barrier as it were, of the pure concepts of the understanding, or the *categories* as Kant calls them, following Aristotelean terminology. Later in the *Kritik* he designates the appearances as *phenomena*, and the things in themselves as *noumena*. We can know the phenomena, but with the pure speculative reason we cannot know the noumena.

A consequence of taking objects in this two-fold sense, i.e. as phenomenal and as noumenal, is that, for instance, the law of causality applies only to the phenomenal object and not to the noumenal. Thus e.g. the will in its visible acts is not free, but in itself it is free.

By this Copernican revolution, Kant has answered the questions : 'how are pure mathematics and pure physics possible ? ' The question 'is metaphysics possible ? ' he has answered in the negative as far as its major component is concerned. He writes[2] :

---

[1] *Kritik*, B xix. Kemp Smith's translation.
[2] *Kritik*, B xxii. Kemp Smith's translation.

This attempt to alter the procedure which has hitherto prevailed in metaphysics, by completely revolutionising it in accordance with the example set by the geometers and physicists, forms indeed the main purpose of this critique of pure speculative reason.

His revolutionising of the procedure of metaphysics has resulted in the denial of the traditional metaphysics. Later, in discussing the antinomies of pure reason, he goes on to substantiate this claim that metaphysics is beyond our reach, by ostensibly demonstrating that whenever we try to venture out into the realms of metaphysics we become involved in hopeless contradictions, so that progress is impossible.

Accordingly the traditional subjects of enquiry by the speculative reason, namely, God, Freedom, and Immortality, are abolished. But Kant is careful to point out that in abolishing knowledge he is making room for faith.[1] The practical reason can take over where the speculative reason is compelled to leave off. The activity of the practical reason Kant develops in his ethical works. Thus Kant gave a powerful impetus to the doctrine of the sharp dichotomy between the world of ordinary facts on the one hand, and the world of morals and emotions and values, on the other, a dichotomy which runs through so much of modern philosophy.

The *Kritik* proper begins with the Transcendental Aesthetic in which space and time are made out as *a priori* principles of knowledge, as pure forms of sensuous intuition. Space and time do not exist of themselves or represent any property of things in themselves. Space and time are forms of experience of outer and inner sense respectively.

Then Kant goes on to the deduction of the categories themselves, 'the most difficult task ever undertaken in aid of metaphysics,' he tells us.[2] He arrives at the conclusion that they are twelve in number. He attempts to show that the transcendental unity of apperception and the systematic unity of objects necessitate the categories. They are, as it were the pre-suppositions for the unity of experience.

[1] *Kritik*, B xxx.
[2] *Proleg.*, p. 7.

Such then in outline is the vast theme of Kant's *Critique of Pure Reason*. But, let us stress, his theory of metaphysics, which is its main content, has its starting point in what the author himself calls an *experiment*. It is time to enquire more minutely into this starting point.

### The Origin of the a priori Concepts

Let us recapitulate what Kant said about the origin of the *a priori* concepts of the understanding in his outline of the subject in the Preface to the 2nd Edition of the *Kritik*.

*As regards metaphysics* he speaks of objects conforming to 'the constitution of our faculty of intuition' and he goes on :
understanding has rules which I must pre-suppose as being in me prior to objects being given to me, and therefore as being *a priori*. They find expression in *a priori* concepts to which all objects of experience necessarily conform, and with which they must agree.[1]
Although Kant does not use the word we may fairly describe the pure concepts of the understanding as 'innate.'

*As regards physics* Kant is not at all clear precisely from whence the *a priori* concepts come. He tells us that reason must approach Nature not as a pupil, but as an appointed judge compelling witnesses to answer questions which he has himself formulated. But from whence does the judge get the questions ?

Kant indicates vaguely from time to time that the principles of judgment in physics proceed ultimately from the same pure *a priori* concepts of the understanding which serve in metaphysics. But he is never very clear about just how. Although the *a priori* judgments of physics served as the paradigm on which Kant reconstructed metaphysics ' by way of experiment,' yet subsequently he becomes much more explicit about the *a priori* concepts in metaphysics than he is about the origin of the *a priori* concepts in physics.

This is a crucial matter and we will return to this subject presently, after we have answered another question.

### Are the Laws of Mathematics and Physics a priori Synthetic Judgments ?

[1] B xvii. Kemp Smith's translation.

We have seen how Kant's theory of metaphysics was an experiment. He reconstructed metaphysics on the model of what he supposed mathematics and modern physics to be. He believed that the propositions of these two established sciences are *a priori* synthetic judgments. Since one of the main purposes of Kant's argument in the *Kritik* is to show *how a priori* synthetic judgments are possible, it would be very serious for Kant's whole philosophy if it turned out on closer scrutiny that no such judgments exist.

Kant claims that all mathematical judgments without exception are synthetic.[1] But his arguments for this in the *Kritik* are not compelling, and reflection suggests rather the view that they are analytic, or tautological, or the result of an intellectual act of abstraction. Whatever be the exact truth of the matter, the hard and fast Kantian dictum that they are *a priori* synthetic would seem to be merely dogmatic.[2]

Thus one of the supports of Kant's contention that metaphysical propositions are *a priori* synthetic judgments is weakened when the analogy of mathematics is seriously questioned.

The other leg of Kant's argument, that there are *a priori* synthetic judgments, comes from natural science. This is Kant's mainstay.

To what extent is Kant right about natural science?

### How is Physics Possible?

We must examine in more detail than hitherto what Kant has to say on this crucial subject.

His claim is, of course, that since the 17th century revolution effected by Galileo and his contemporaries, the science of Nature, i.e. physics, has consisted of *a priori* synthetic judgments. We have already discussed the account of this matter which Kant gives in the 2nd Edition Preface, about man

---

[1] *Kritik*, Intro. V.
[2] This applies to Euclidean geometry, the only system known in Kant's day. See Ch. XII for the case of non-Euclidean geometry.

approaching Nature with principles of judgment based upon fixed laws, constraining Nature to give answer to questions of reason's own determining.

In various places in the subsequent *Kritik* he attempts to be more explicit, but, as already indicated, without much clearness or consistency.

In the Transcendental Deduction of the 1st Edition we read:

The order and regularity in the appearances, which we entitle *nature*, we ourselves introduce. . . . Although we learn many laws through experience, they are only special determinations of still higher laws, and the highest of these, under which the others all stand, issue *a priori* from the understanding itself. They are not borrowed from experience ; on the contrary they have to confer upon appearances their conformity to law, and so to make experience possible. *Thus the understanding is something more than a power of formulating rules through comparison of appearances ; it is itself the lawgiver of nature.*[1]

In another place he writes :

Appearances are subject to no law of connection save that which the connecting faculty prescribes.[2]

Again he writes :

Even natural laws, viewed as principles of the empirical employment of understanding, carry with them an expression of necessity, and so contain at least the suggestion of a determination from grounds which are valid *a priori* and antecedently to all experience. The laws of nature, indeed, one and all, without exception, stand under higher principles of understanding. They simply apply the latter to special cases (in the field) of appearance. These principles alone supply the concept which contains the condition, and as it were the exponent, of a rule in general. What experience gives is the instance which stands under the rule.[3]

And more explicitly still :

By nature, in the empirical sense, we understand the connection of appearances as regards their existence according to necessary

[1] *Kritik,* A 125–6. Kemp Smith's translation. Italics not in original.
[2] *Kritik,* B 164. Kemp Smith's translation.
[3] *Kritik,* B 198. Kemp Smith's translation.

rules, that is, according to laws. There are certain laws which first make a nature possible, and these laws are *a priori*. Empirical laws can exist and be discovered only through experience, and indeed in consequence of those original laws through which experience itself first becomes possible.[1]

A curious feature will be noticed about Kant's remarks on natural science. He starts off with the blunt assertion that the laws and principles of physics are *a priori* synthetic judgments and cites the activity of Galileo, Torricelli, etc. Later in the Introduction[2] we find him citing the conservation of mass and Newton's 3rd Law as examples of *a priori* synthetic judgments constituting principles of physics. He repeats these examples in the next section of the Introduction[3] where he describes such laws as being propositions found at the beginning of empirical physics and constituting in themselves a *physica pura*. In connection with the First Analogy he attempts a transcendental proof of the Law of Conservation of Mass. It is clear that here he regards such laws of physics as *a priori* synthetic judgments of the understanding.

But in other passages we have quoted he seems to be wavering. In A 126, B 198, and still more in B 263, he suggests that the principles of physical science do not themselves proceed *a priori* from the understanding itself, but in some way stand under the pure *a priori* categories, or are special determinations of them.

In the *Prolegomena*, which was written after the first edition of the *Kritik*, he distinguishes physics from the propaedeutic of physics, the pure science of Nature, which precedes all physics. Everything in the pure science of Nature is to be *a priori* and necessary, whereas in physics there are empirical principles.

Sometimes in the *Kritik* he recognises this division into the pure and the empirical, and sometimes he ignores it. Or perhaps it would be more accurate to say that he cannot decide where to draw the line between the two. Sometimes he draws

[1] *Kritik*, B 263.
[2] *Kritik*, B 17–18.
[3] *Kritik*, B 21 n.

it so high that only the metaphysical categories are *a priori*. Sometimes it is drawn so low that even laws like the conservation of mass and Newton's laws of motion are *a priori*.

## Kant's Dilemma

Let us enquire more closely into Kant's difficulty in this matter.

Having propounded the Copernican revolution in natural science, Kant made a great blunder which ruined his whole system. It is one thing to discover the *a priori* character of the natural laws. It is another to trace the *a priori* character to its source. Kant was obsessed with the idea that to be *a priori* synthetic could only arise from innateness in the mind. This obsession landed him in a hopeless dilemma.

Kant wanted to say that all the universal laws of physics were innate principles of judgment to which Nature was made to conform. But he found as he went on that this raised great difficulties, and he tried to moderate the doctrine. Nevertheless he is often forced to lapse back into the old view that all the natural principles are *a priori* synthetic judgments of the understanding.

As we have already pointed out, we would expect Kant to say that such laws as the conservation of mass and Newton's 3rd law were not pure *a priori* principles of the understanding, but only special determinations of such principles. But in fact in the passage in the Introduction and elsewhere he holds the laws themselves to be *a priori* synthetic judgments. They are plainly synthetic. So far as their *a priori* nature is concerned he holds this because of their necessity. No experience can yield the character of necessity: 'Experience does indeed show that one appearance customarily follows upon another, but not that this sequence is necessary.'[1] Hence they must be *a priori* in origin. These two laws, the conservation of mass and Newton's 3rd law, are representative of all the established principles of physics. What applies to them must apply to all the established principles.

---

[1] *Kritik*, A 112.

It is fairly plain that Kant commenced with the view that all the principles of physics are necessary and therefore must issue *a priori* from the understanding. But later, overwhelmed by the complexity of the *a priori* machinery of the understanding which this would entail, he modifies this by making laws learnt through experience special determinations of higher laws, while the highest are those which issue *a priori* from the understanding itself.

He writes:

However exaggerated and absurd it may sound, to say that the understanding is itself the source of the laws of nature, and so of its formal unity, such an assertion is none the less correct, and is in keeping with the object to which it refers, namely, experience. Certainly, empirical laws, as such, can never derive their origin from pure understanding. That is as little possible as to understand completely the inexhaustible multiplicity of appearances merely by reference to the pure form of sensible intuition. But all empirical laws are only special determinations of the pure laws of understanding, under which, and according to the norm of which, they first become possible. Through them appearances take on an orderly character, just as these same appearances, despite the differences of their empirical form, must none the less, always be in harmony with the pure form of sensibility.[1]

This is in accord with the distinction suggested in the *Prolegomena* between physics and the pure science of Nature which precedes all physics.

But here in this vague state he continually leaves the subject. He does not develop the distinction and give examples. And on those rare occasions when he does come to be more specific, as in Introduction V, he abandons the distinction and cites particular laws of physics as examples of *a priori* synthetic judgments.

All through the *Kritik*, whenever he refers to the subject, he is obviously uneasy about this matter ; he does not know whether to try to put in all the laws of physics as innate in association with the categories, or whether to say the most universal laws

[1] *Kritik*, A 127–8. Kemp Smith's translation.

are innate but the particular laws are empirical although standing under the higher principles.

Kant anticipates that the pure concepts of the understanding will be few in number:

' These *a priori* possessions of the understanding,' he writes, ' since they have not to be sought for without, cannot remain hidden from us, and in all probability are sufficiently small in extent to allow of our apprehending them in their completeness.'[1]

But if he has to put all the established laws of physics into the *a priori* possession of the understanding he will bid fair to wreck the whole system through the multiplicity and complexity this will involve.

On the other hand the existence of the particular laws of physics and their *a priori* character served, along with the supposedly similar character of mathematical judgments, as the paradigm on which he built up his theory of metaphysics. He cannot now turn around and deny this *a priori* character to the physical laws. Yet its continued acceptance raises grave difficulties.

Kant is in a dilemma, and within the bounds of his own philosophy there seems to be no way out. He shuffles and vacillates all through the *Critique of Pure Reason* whenever the matter comes up.

## The True Character of the Physical Laws

Kant everywhere assumes that necessity can only arise from being *a priori* in the sense of an *a priori* possession of the understanding, an innate possession we might say. *This assumption is the fundamental source of his troubles.* For although Kant does not realise it, a law can be *a priori* and synthetic, and hence necessary, and yet not issue from the understanding as a pure concept. Kant quite overlooks the fact that the constitution of the mind is not the only source of the *a priori* (if in fact it is a source at all). For a law can be *a priori* and synthetic on other grounds, as is so clearly revealed by many modern systems of philosophy.

---

[1] *Kritik*, B 26. Kemp Smith's translation.

For instance, a law could be based on necessity arising from the conventional usage of language, i.e. based on our determination to use words in a certain conventional way. Some philosophers nowadays hold that this is the case with the propositions of logic.[1] These propositions, they say, are in fact tautologies and hence can never be false. Their truth and necessity do not depend in any way on innateness in the mind or on the structure of the universe, but are rather what we might call 'sociological.' (More will be said on this theme in Ch. VIII).

Again the necessity of a law could be based on a determination held by a person, or held in common by a number of people with some common purpose, to make Nature conform to some pre-determined law. Thus would the *a priori* and synthetic character arise from a Procrustean bed procedure, without any connection at all with innate judgments of the understanding. This we have suggested in Ch. III is in fact the case with modern physics. The physicists, with the common purpose of utility and power over Nature, subject Nature to their Procrustean treatment and hence arrive at laws which are necessary in the sense of binding, or at least temporarily binding.

*The truth is that the laws of physics are a priori synthetic propositions, but not a priori and synthetic judgments of the understanding.[2] Kant confused these two issues and to this confusion the downfall of his philosophy may be traced.*

### Why Kant Erred

It was no doubt Kant's Rationalist background which prompted him to identify the natural laws with the innate judgments of the understanding. Leibnitz, the great exponent of Rationalist philosophy, had held that experiment served merely as a confirmation of innate reason. He writes[3] :

[1] The fact that these philosophers would hold too that such propositions are not synthetic but analytic does not affect our present argument.

[2] And hence are not limited in any direct way by reference to Kant's twelve categories.

[3] *New Essays on the Human Understanding.*

If certain events can be foreseen before we have made any trial of them, it is clear that we contribute in those cases something of our own. The senses, although they are necessary for all our actual knowledge, are not sufficient to give us the whole of it, since the senses never give anything but instances, that is to say particular or individual truths. Now all the instances which confirm a general truth, however numerous they may be, are not sufficient to establish the universal necessity of this same truth, for it does not follow that what happened before will happen in the same way again.

Pure mathematics, particularly arithmetic and geometry, also logic, metaphysics, and morals, are full of truths whose proofs do not depend on instances, although without the senses it may never have occurred to us to think of them.

' Consequently proof of them can only arise from inner principles, which are called innate.' Leibnitz goes on. ' It is true that we must not imagine that we can read in the soul these eternal laws of reason as in an open book, as the edict of the praetor can be read in his *album* without trouble or deep scrutiny. But it is enough that we can find them in ourselves by dint of attention, opportunities for which are afforded by the senses. *The success of experiments serves also as a confirmation of reason, more or less as verifications serve in arithmetic to help us to avoid erroneous calculation when the reasoning is long.*'

Kant had rejected the doctrine of innate ideas in the mind, and hence also Leibnitz's contention that the laws of Nature, like those of geometry, are innate. Kant held instead that there are in the mind innate categories of judgment, and from these the natural laws proceed, immediately or mediately. Change 'innate ideas' to 'pure concepts of the understanding' in the foregoing passages from Leibnitz, and we have a doctrine not so very different from the Kantian.

Kant's Copernican revolution is not then so novel viewed from the Rationalist point of view as it is from the Empiricist. Only in the consequences for metaphysics do the Leibnitzian and Kantian doctrines differ greatly. As far as physics is concerned they both explain the supposed necessity of the laws by an appeal to innateness, although they each appeal differently. Kant's theory of physics leaves the science more freedom than does Leibnitz's and is much closer to what we have held to be the true theory.

The Empiricist philosophers, it might be noted, in their reaction from the Rationalists, swung to the other extreme. They denied innateness and the *a priori* in any shape or form, and hence were in difficulties to explain the necessity of the natural laws. The problem of induction was indeed very acute for the Empiricists. The Kantian and the neo-Kantian Procrustean theories are intermediate between these two extremes of Rationalist and Empiricist.

It was just possible at the time in which Kant was writing, i.e. the latter half of the 18th century, to hold such views as his about the laws of Nature being in some way intuitive. The principal universal laws current in Kant's day were such principles as Newton's three laws of motion, the law of gravitation, and the law of the conservation of matter. It is just possible to hold with some show of plausibility that these laws are intuitive.[1] But had Kant lived 50 years later the great multiplicity and exotic character of the laws which were then gaining currency would have effectively dispelled ideas of innateness from his mind. No one could hold for a moment that e.g. the laws of electromagnetic induction are in any way intuitive. If, in addition, Kant could have been aware that many of the fundamental laws, held in the 18th century to be securely established, are today no longer generally held, then his notion of innateness would have been completely dispelled. The same considerations apply of course to Leibnitz's earlier and even less satisfactory theory of innateness.

Had Kant had this foreknowledge he might have propounded the Copernican revolution in *physics* against the Empiricists, without appealing to the pure *a priori* concepts of the understanding, and hence without his disastrous Copernican revolution in *metaphysics*. For, if the *a priori* synthetic character of physics does not require innate principles of the understanding, Kant would no longer have had reason to think that all our knowledge comes from the imposition of the categories on the real world. So we would not have had the

---

[1] It is remarkable that even today some authors of elementary text books of physics attempt to make the principles of mechanics seem self-apparent, and upbraid the Aristoteleans for not having ' seen ' them.

separation of the knowable phenomena from the unknowable noumena, with the consequent problem of the relation of noumena to phenomena. (It would be natural to say that the noumena *caused* the phenomenal experiences to which the categories gave form. But cause itself is a category, so that the relation of noumena to phenomena cannot be causal. It is an insoluble problem for Kant). Without the doctrine of the principles of the understanding we would not have had the denial of the possibility of transcending possible experience, so that metaphysics would still be possible.

Had this taken place, then later philosophers would not have been repelled by Kant's whole egocentric system, and might not have been blind to the one great truth which lies at the bottom of his philosophy. For, because of the general prejudice against Kant, the genuine Copernican revolution in physical science, which Kant detected, has been almost entirely overlooked, although it could have been most illuminating. Had more notice been taken of Kant's fundamental doctrine, the course of post-Kantian philosophy might have been quite different, particularly, as we shall see in later chapters, for neo-Scholastic philosophy for which the Kantian doctrine has a particular relevance. But unfortunately, as we have already remarked, students of Kant have been more concerned with the minutiae of Kant's philosophy, and with the interpretation of his doctrines in terms of the traditional philosophical controversies, than with an examination of the foundations of his system. The general failure to get down to fundamentals has obscured Kant's permanent contribution to the course of philosophy.

It is interesting to notice, too, that had Kant lived a century before he did, he would probably not have detected the *a priori* nature of the physical laws at all. For the ' Copernican revolution ' in modern physics grew up from very small and obscure beginnings. Galileo, Newton and most of their contemporaries were probably themselves unconscious of the real character of what they were doing. Newton, particularly, was as much medieval as modern in his *conscious* thought.

It was wise Kimri, so it is said, who saw beneath the earth where the future is being prepared, and it is there that we too must look. Kant was the wise Kimri who looked beneath the surface of modern science and saw a glimmer of the truth.

If Kant had not detected this, if he had not thought that the natural laws were *a priori* and synthetic, he would probably not have thought that metaphysical propositions also were of this character, since the physical paradigm is the starting off point for his theory of metaphysics.

Thus Kant would probably not have propounded his system in anything like its actual form, with its denial of metaphysics, had he lived at any other time than when he did. There is, strictly, no history of philosophy, which is timeless ; but there is a natural history of philosophising.

### Kant's Achievement

Kant's great contribution to philosophy was to point out the revolution in natural science effected by Galileo and Bacon and their successors. This stands in principle even though all the rest of his philosophy wither away. Prior to Galileo people had been concerned with reading laws *in* Nature. After Galileo they read laws *into* Nature. His clear recognition of this fact makes Kant the fundamental philosopher of the modern world. *It is the greatest contribution to the philosophia perennis since St. Thomas.* But this has to be dug patiently out of Kant. Kant himself so overlaid and obscured his discovery that it has ever since gone well nigh unrecognised.

We may, in fact we must, refrain from following Kant in his doctrine of metaphysics. The modelling of metaphysics on physics was his great experiment. The experiment is manifestly a failure, although a noble failure, in pursuit of what he mistakenly believed to be the best interests of metaphysics.

But, putting the metaphysical experiment aside, the principle on which it was founded abides, the principle of our categorial activity. Later, in Ch. XVIII, we will see in more detail how this principle is essential to the modern development of the *philosophia perennis.*

Kant was truly the philosopher of the modern world when we look judiciously at his work. As a motto for the *Kritik* Kant actually quotes a passage from Francis Bacon in which is laid down the programme for the pursuit of human utility and power.[1] As we saw in Ch. IV, it was Bacon above all who gave articulate expression to the *spirit* behind the new science. Now we see that it was Kant who, for the first time, divined the *nature* of the new science. *If Bacon was the politician of the new régime, Kant was its philosopher, although a vastly over-ambitious one.*

What was needed was for someone to point out clearly the 'otherness' of post-Galilean physical science, i.e. the fact that it is, in a sense, cut off from the rest of the world, and is the creation of man himself.[2] The new science has no metaphysical foundations and no metaphysical implications. Kant had the clue to this 'otherness' in the categorial theory, but he took the rest of the world with him in the course of the revolution and hence only succeeded in the end in missing the point.

Most people since then, rightly sceptical about Kant's wholesale revolution, have been quite hostile to the Kantian system in general. Others, perhaps without realising it, have rewritten the revolution in their own terms, and thus have perpetuated Kant's principal errors (as e.g. Wittgenstein in his *Tractatus Logico-Philosophicus*[3].)

A thorough sifting out of Kant has long been required in order to separate the gold from the dross.

What is needed is not a wholesale revolution, like Kant's, but a *limited* revolution. This, it has been suggested in Ch. III, can be effected along the lines of Eddington's Procrustean bed theory, which is what Kant should have said, and perhaps what he wanted to say, but what he could not quite manage to articulate.

Kant's mistake was to think that the world *had* to be transformed to know it. The truth is that the world *may* be transformed, if we so dictate, and then it is not to *know* the world but to *control* it.

---

[1] The passage is quoted again in this work on p. 47.
[2] See p. 53.     [3] See Ch. VII.

The story of Kant and his problem is the story of a man who saw far but not quite far enough. In him a great enlightenment was mingled with a great darkness. We shall see in Ch. XVIII in what way the *purged* Kant is the successor of St. Thomas and the completer of his great edifice.

# CHAPTER VII

# THE NEO-KANTIANS

*Custom, then, is the great guide of human life.*

DAVID HUME.

LET us here consider briefly some representative modern philosophers who may be described as neo-Kantian, in that thay all advance doctrines involving categorial interpretations of the world, but differing in various ways from Kant's. We will find everywhere that the evolution after Kant was towards a more elastic and liberal and less compulsory theory of categories.

Following this we will turn a backward glance on Hume.

## Wittgenstein

Wittgenstein, in the latter part of his early and somewhat enigmatic work, the *Tractatus Logico–Philosophicus*, holds what may be called neo-Kantian views. (It is not to be supposed that Wittgenstein would necessarily hold to the doctrines in this form to-day). For the most part Wittgenstein here appears as an inferior Kant, lacking Kant's breadth of vision. But his variations on the Kantian principles are interesting.

Wittgenstein, like Kant, proceeds not by exploring the world but by imposing a framework on it, so that the world behind the framework, i.e. the real world of metaphysics, is always beyond our reach.

' All propositions,' he writes[1] ' such as the law of causation, the law of continuity in nature, the law of least expenditure in nature, etc., etc., all these are *a priori* intuitions of possible forms of the propositions of science.

[1] *Tractatus* (London, 1922), 6· 34 ff.

Newtonian mechanics, for example, brings the description of the universe to a unified form. Let us imagine a white surface with irregular black spots. We now say : Whatever kind of picture these make I can always get as near as I like to its description, if I cover the surface with a sufficiently fine square network and now say of every square that it is white or black. In this way I shall have brought the description of the surface to a unified form. This form is arbitrary, because I could have applied with equal success a net with a triangular or hexagonal mesh. It can happen that the description would have been simpler with the aid of a triangular mesh ; that is to say we might have described the surface more accurately with a triangular, and coarser, than with the finer square mesh, or *vice versa*, and so on. To the different networks correspond different systems of describing the world. Mechanics determine a form of description by saying : All propositions in the description of the world must be obtained in a given way from a number of given propositions—the mechanical axioms. It thus provides the bricks for building the edifice of science, and says : Whatever building thou wouldst erect, thou shalt construct it in some manner with these bricks and these alone.

(As with the system of numbers one must be able to write down any arbitrary number, so with the system of mechanics one must be able to write down any arbitrary physical proposition.)

And now we see the relative position of logic and mechanics. (We could construct the network out of figures of different kinds, as out of triangles and hexagons together). That a picture like that instanced above can be described by a network of a given form asserts *nothing* about the picture. (For this holds of every picture of this kind). But *this* does characterise the picture, the fact, namely, that it can be *completely* described by a definite net of *definite* fineness.

So too the fact that it can be described by Newtonian mechanics asserts nothing about the world ; but *this* asserts something, namely, that it can be described in that particular way in which as a matter of fact it is described. The fact, too, that it can be described more simply by one system of mechanics than by another says something about the world.'

And again[1] :

' Laws like the law of causation, etc. treat of the network and not of what the network describes.'

[1] *Tractatus*, 6· 35.

This is a very clear enunciation of the doctrine that modern physics consists of categories, or Procrustean beds, a doctrine with which we have already dealt in some detail in Ch. III. There, however, we derived it from purely domestic considerations in the science of physics, and not at the dictates of a more general pre-conceived theory of knowledge, which seems to be the impelling force behind such writers as Wittgenstein.

Wittgenstein maintains a similar categorial doctrine with regard to logic. He holds that we impose logic on the world like the network in physical science. Necessity is thereby in logic and not in the world. In the world itself, he believes, there are no necessary connections at all :

'A necessity for one thing to happen because another has happened does not exist. There is only *logical* necessity.'[1] And again : 'Outside logic all is accident.'[2]

Further :

The propositions of logic are tautologies and therefore say nothing. (They are analytical propositions.)[3]

Another contemporary philosopher, A. J. Ayer,[4] expresses a similar doctrine by saying that the necessary propositions of logic (and mathematics) merely express our determination to use words in a certain way.

It might be noted in passing that the empiricist logician, John Stuart Mill, denied that there was real necessity even in logic and mathematics. He believed that the laws of logic and mathematics are empirical generalisations from a vast number of instances. Wittgenstein rejects this extreme doctrine. He admits that there is necessity and authority and certainty in the propositions of logic and mathematics, but he refuses to impute this authority to the constitution of the world ; instead he makes it reside in language. From whence language derives this authority, and how it comes to exercise

---

[1] *Ibid*. 6· 37.
[2] *Ibid*. 6· 3.
[3] *Ibid*. 6· 1 and 6· 11.
[4] See his *Language, Truth and Logic* (London, 1936).

it, is not made clear.[1]   Yet Wittgenstein has no doubts about
the fact :

If we know the logical syntax of any sign language then all the
propositions of logic are already given.

we are told.[2]   The tautologous propositions of logic act as
centres of organisation in describing the world :

The logical propositions describe the scaffolding of the world,
or rather they present it.[3]

We can compare this situation with that in Kant's philosophy.   The categories for Kant are innate in the mind, or
understanding, and are imposed by the mind on the world.
So too, with Wittgenstein, the logical propositions are imposed
on the world.   But now the propositions, instead of being
innate in the mind, are associated with language.   The system
of Wittgenstein is thus more liberal than that of Kant.   Kant's
categories are embedded in the constitution of the mind, and
are immutable and inescapable.   Wittgenstein's categories
spring from language ; consequently they are not so immutable
and inescapable, but rather sociological and customary.   On
the other hand they are certainly not capricious, since custom
and convention are, as a rule, moderately stable, and sometimes
very stable.

With both Kant and Wittgenstein, the world lying behind
the categorial frame is beyond our intellectual reach.   Metaphysics for Kant is impossible.   We cannot penetrate into the
noumenal world with the speculative reason.   Likewise for
Wittgenstein metaphysics is meaningless.   It is in fact
' unspeakable.'   For both of them the world of morals lies in
the region beyond, so that morals are not subject to the pure
intellect.   They both effect a violent dichotomy of the world,
with science and knowledge on one side, and life and emotion
on the other.

### Lewis

A contemporary American philosopher, C. I. Lewis, in his

[1] See Ch. VIII.
[2] *Tractatus*, 6· 124.
[3] *Ibid.* 6· 124.

interesting book, *Mind and the World Order*, carries the neo-Kantian movement another step further than Wittgenstein. Wittgenstein's categories had a linguistic basis, which meant that they were, so to speak, sociological in origin. The categories of Lewis on the other hand have, as well as a sociological, a more specifically pragmatic sanction. Lewis's system is therefore still more liberal and flexible than that of Wittgenstein, which in its turn was much more flexible than that of Kant.

Lewis writes :

Experience does not categorise itself. The criteria of interpretation are of the mind : they are imposed upon the given by our active attitude.[1]

And further :

Philosophy is the study of the *a priori* and is thus the mind's formulation of its own active attitudes.[2]

The fact that there is accord between different minds does not entail that there is some universal pattern of human reason, nor a realm of transcendental concepts, nor initial self-evident principles. For :

The coincidence of our fundamental criteria and principles is the combined result of the similarity of human animals, and of their primal interests, and the similarities of the experience with which they have to deal. More explicitly, it represents one result of the interplay between these two ; the coincidence of human modes of behaviour, particularly when the interests which such behaviour serves involve co-operation. . . .

Our common understanding and our common world may be, in part, created in response to our need to act together and to comprehend one another. . . .

*Indeed our categories are almost as much a social product as is language, and in something like the same sense.* . . .

. . . That the categories are fundamental in such wise that the social process can neither create nor alter them, is a rationalistic prejudice without foundation. . . .[3]

Again he writes :

. . . What is *a priori* is prior to experience in almost the same

[1] *Mind and the World Order* (New York, 1929), p. 14.
[2] *Ibid.* p. 24.
[3] *Ibid.* pp. 20–22.

sense that purpose is. Purposes are not dictated by the content of the given ; they are our own. Yet purposes must take their shape and have their realization in terms of experience ; the content of the given is not irrelevant to them.[1]

Lewis goes on to expand his pragmatic theory of the origin of the categories.

Though a categorial principle must in the nature of the case be prior to the particular experience, it nevertheless represents an attitude which the mind has taken in the light of past experience as a whole, and one which would even be susceptible of change if confronted with some pervasive alteration in the general character of what is presented. . . .[2]

There follows an interesting illustration of mass as the criterion of the physical. Lewis proceeds :

This legislative attitude of mind is clearly one which is taken because, our experience on the whole being what it is, this principle helps to render it intelligible, and behaviour in accord with it is normally successful. The mind must bring to experience whatever serves as the criteria of interpretation—of the real, as of the right, the beautiful, and the valid. *The content of experience cannot evaluate or interpret itself.* Nevertheless the validity of such interpretation must reflect the character of experience in general *and meet the pragmatic test of value as a guide to action.*

Traditional rationalism, observing that any principles which should serve as ultimate criterion, or determine categorial inter-pretation, must be prior to and independent of the experience to which it applies, has supposed that such principles must be innate and so discoverable by some sort of direct inspection. If a canon of their truth is requisite, this must be supplied by something of a higher order than experience, such as self-evidence or the natural light of reason.[3]

On the other hand[4] : The fallacy of pure empiricism is the converse of that which rationalism commits. In seeking to identify the real with what is given in experience, apart from construction or interpretation by the mind, and to elicit general principles directly from the content of experience, empiricism condemns itself to a vicious circle. . . . For when the empiricist supposes that laws

[1] *Ibid.* p. 24.
[2] *Ibid.* pp. 26–27.
[3] *Ibid.* p. 25.
[4] *Ibid.* pp. 27–29.

or principles can be derived simply by generalization from experience he *means* to refer only to *veridical* experience, forgetting that without the criterion of legislative principle experience cannot first be sorted into veridical and illusory. . . .

Generalization from experience always presumes that the categorial interpretation already has been made.

Similarly with other problems of philosophy :

The nature of the good can be learned from experience only if the content of experience be first classified into good and bad, or grades of better and worse.[1] Such classification or grading already involves the legislative application of the same principle which is sought.[2]

The world of experience is not given in experience : it is constructed by thought from the data of sense. This reality which everybody knows reflects the structure of human intelligence as much as it does the nature of the independently given sensory content. It is a whole in which mind and what is given to mind already meet and are interwoven. The datum of our philosophic study is not the " buzzing, blooming confusion " on which the infant first opens his eyes, not the thin experience of immediate sensation, but the thick experience of everyday life. . . . The buzzing, blooming confusion could not become reality for an oyster.[3]

Unlike Kant, for whom the categories were fixed and immutable, the categories for Lewis are relatively fluid.[4]

' Concepts and principles reveal themselves as instruments of interpretation ; their meaning lies in the empirical consequences of the active attitude. The categories are ways of dealing with what is given to the mind, and if they had no practical consequences the mind would never use them. Since philosophy seeks to formulate what is implicit in mind's everyday interpretations, we may test the significance of any philosophic principle, and pave the way for determining its truth, if we ask : How would experience be different if this should be correct than if it should be false ?

[1] cf. Plato : *Meno*, 80. Plato drew attention in ethics to the same considerations as does Lewis. For Plato, however, the principles are eternal and immutable. We have become acquainted with them in a previous existence, and learning now is really reminiscence. For Lewis on the other hand the principles are not in any way embedded in the universe, but have only a social and pragmatic sanction.

[2] *Ibid.* p. 29.

[3] *Ibid.* pp. 29–30.

[4] *Ibid.* p. 31.

or, How differently should we orient ourselves to experience and deal with it if this should be so than if it should not be so ?

Lewis's attitude to metaphysics is similar to that of all Kantians. Metaphysics is impossible according to Kant, unspeakable according to Wittgenstein, and nonsensical according to Lewis :

Metaphysical issues which supposedly concern what is transcendent of experience altogether, must inevitably turn out to be issues wrongly taken. . . . A predication of reality to what transcends experience completely and in every sense, is not problematic ; it is nonsense.[1]

In understanding Lewis's neo-Kantian philosophy the pragmatic basis must always be borne in mind :

The significance of such fundamental conceptions must always be practical because thought and action are continuous, and because no other origin of them can be plausible than an origin which reflects their bearing on experience.[2]

The system of Lewis is a happy combination of pragmatism with Kantian categorial philosophy. It is more mellow than that of other exponents, such as Kant himself and Wittgenstein. There is, as we shall see, much truth in what Lewis has said. But like most modern philosophers Lewis has extended his system beyond its proper field, and thereby rendered it quite unacceptable as it stands. Nevertheless, when much more moderate claims are made for it, his categorial pragmatism undoubtedly throws much light on the world and society.

## H. Poincaré

In a chapter on the neo-Kantians some mention must be made of the monumental work of Poincaré[3]. He does not treat primarily of philosophy and the world in general. He directs his attention rather to mathematics and the physical sciences. But within that field, which is indeed the field from

---

[1] *Ibid.* pp. 31–32. We shall have more to say on this doctrine in discussing logical positivism. (Ch. X).

[2] *Ibid.* p. 34.

[3] See principally his *Foundations of Science* (Eng. Tr.) comprising three works : *Science and Hypothesis*, *The Value of Science*, and *Science and Method*.

which Kant started, Poincaré shows himself a worthy successor of his great master.

Consider this passage from Poincaré[1] :

It is often said experiments must be made without a preconceived idea. That is impossible. Not only would it make all experiment barren, but that would be attempted which could not be done.

Compare this with Kant's homily on the pupil learning openmouthed what Nature has to tell him, and the stern judge compelling witnesses to answer questions of his own devising.[2] Poincaré has divined the same feature of modern physics which struck Kant so forcibly.

But where Kant went on to lay down rigid and inescapable categories, Poincaré keeps the structure loose, in much the same way as we have seen done by Lewis. Poincaré's categorial system is conventional, and therefore relatively fixed. It is neither unalterable on the one hand, nor capricious on the other.

For instance in discussing geometry[3] he writes :

The axioms of geometry are neither synthetic *a priori* judgments nor experimental facts.

In saying they are not synthetic *a priori* judgments he is breaking free from the Kantian rigidity (and is thus incidentally admitting non-Euclidean geometry, which strict Kantians could not admit). In denying that they are experimental facts he is dissociating himself from the extreme empiricists like John Stuart Mill.

He goes on :

They are *conventions* ; our choice among all possible conventions is *guided* by experimental facts ; but it remains *free* and is limited only by the necessity of avoiding all contradiction. Thus it is that the postulates can remain *rigorously* true even though the experimental laws which have determined their adoption are only approximative.

In other words *the axioms of geometry* (I do not speak of those of arithmetic) *are merely disguised definitions*.

[1] *Foundations of Science*, p. 129.
[2] See p. 77.
[3] *Ibid.* p. 65.

Then what are we to think of that question : Is the Euclidean geometry true ?

It has no meaning.

As well ask whether the metric system is true and the old measures false ; whether Cartesian co-ordinates are true and polar co-ordinates false. One geometry can not be more true than another ; it can only be *more convenient*.

The reader may or may not agree with this account of the foundations of science as applied to the status of Euclidean geometry,[1] but nevertheless this account, taken to indicate Poincaré's general views about the foundations of science, is a very valuable contribution to the subject. It bears an obvious resemblance to the theories of Eddington,[2] while perhaps lacking in the scope and precision which Eddington has given to the subject.

So much for Poincaré's theory of modern physical science. As a theory of physical science it is admirable. But Poincaré follows along the same fatal line as Kant and most of his fellow neo-Kantians. He extends this doctrine from the field of science to things in general. Thus he writes :

Does science teach us the true nature of things ?   .   .   .   ;

To this question, no one would hesitate to reply, no ; but I think we may go farther ; not only science cannot teach us the nature of things ; but nothing is capable of teaching it to us, and if any god knew it, he could not find words to express it. Not only can we not divine the response, but if it were given to us we could understand nothing of it ; I ask myself even whether we really understand the question.[3]

With this truly Wittgensteinian conclusion we must leave Poincaré.

### Eddington

Like Poincaré, Eddington belongs to the line of the neo-Kantians. Eddington himself, it is true, refuses to be labelled as a Kantian.[4] While admitting that his ideas are somewhat

---

[1] See Ch. XII on Non-Euclidean Geometry.
[2] Ch. III.
[3] *Loc. cit.*, p. 350.
[4] Eddington, A. S. : *Philosophy of Physical Science* (Cambridge, 1939), p. 188.

similar to Kant's, he rightly insists that they have a purely scientific grounding. But, from the account we have given of Eddington's Procrustean theory of physics[1] it will be obvious how close is his affinity with the starting point of Kant's philosophy. Kant, like Eddington, detected that the modern physicist is an active agent, not a passive receiver.

Kant hardened the categories into a rigid inescapable system. Eddington keeps his Procrustean beds amenable to change in a manner very like Poincaré. Consequently Eddington is a true neo-Kantian.

Eddington, as seems almost inevitable with neo-Kantians, goes on from his Procrustean categorial principles to advance a mystical, idealist, conception of the real world. But with this we need not be concerned here. It is Eddington's Procrustean theory which is his great contribution.

## Professor Collingwood

Because of its contemporary interest we shall say a word or two about the striking theory of metaphysics advocated by the late Professor R. G. Collingwood.[2] It may fairly be described as neo-Kantian.

Collingwood believes that in any age there lie behind our thinking a number of unperceived absolute pre-suppositions. These pre-suppositions, which he believes change from age to age, function in a manner analogous to Kantian categories in that the world is interpreted in terms of them. When these fundamental categories change, the type of civilisation, and the science which goes with it, are changed accordingly.

It is the business of metaphysics to elucidate the absolute pre-suppositions of each age. Consequently metaphysics and history are linked with the closest bond.[3]

This is a thoroughly relativistic theory of the world. According to Collingwood there can be no question of whether the absolute pre-suppositions of any age are true or false. Such

---

[1] Ch. III.

[2] See principally his *Autobiography* (Oxford, 1939), and *An Essay on Metaphysics*, (Oxford, 1940).

[3] In Ch. XIV we discuss Collingwood's theories on history as a science.

an enquiry is unanswerable. Consequently the conception of 'eternal problems' is abolished from philosophy.

On the question of why the absolute pre-suppositions are subject to change, and thus why we have the major transitions in history, Collingwood writes :

Why do such changes happen ? Briefly, because the absolute pre-suppositions of any given society, at any given phase of its history, form a structure which is subject to 'strains' of greater or less intensity, which are 'taken up' in various ways but never annihilated. If the strains are too great, the structure collapses and is replaced by another, which will be a modification of the old with the destructive strain removed ; a modification not consciously devised but created by a process of unconscious thought.[1]

This is an ingenious theory both of metaphysics and of historical change, but it is open to many objections which there is no need to discuss here.[2] It has served our purpose in illustrating yet another evolution of neo-Kantian philosophy.

### David Hume

While Hume, chronologically, cannot of course be classified as a neo-Kantian, and in fact was rather the philosophical father of Kant, yet it is interesting to examine Hume along with such modern philosophers as Wittgenstein and Lewis, particularly the latter.

It has too often been the fate of David Hume to be treated by the historians of philosophy as merely a sceptic. Certainly he describes himself as such on frequent occasions, but if we look a little more closely into his philosophical writings we find that he goes far beyond the state of mere scepticism and puts forward a positive philosophy of great significance.

We have seen[3] that Immanuel Kant was content to regard Hume as a sceptic who had denied that the causal connection between one thing and another could be found in pure reason

---

[1] *Metaphysics,* p. 48.
[2] We may well retain the principle of pre-suppositions changing from age to age, but we must hesitate to accept the denial that we can question the truth of the pre-suppositions.
[3] Ch. VI.

*a priori*.   Kant thereupon advanced his theory of innate categories as an answer to Hume's supposed scepticism.

But had Kant possessed a rather more intimate acquaintance
with Hume's doctrines he would have attached more significance to the solution that Hume himself puts forward in answer
to his initial sceptical attitude.

Hume concludes that we cannot find the connection between
cause and effect in pure reason.   But, he goes on to add,
instead of looking to Reason we must look to Custom or Habit.
This is the vital addition which distinguishes Hume's philosophy
from mere scepticism, and it is the addition which Kant
tended to ignore.   Hume turns from Reason to the force of
Custom :

' All inferences from experience therefore,' he writes,[1] ' are effects
of custom, not of reasoning.   *Custom, then, is the great guide of human
life.*'

' What is our idea of necessity, when we say that two objects
are necessarily connected together?' he asks[2].   And he concludes
that : ' after a frequent repetition, I find, that upon the appearance
of one of the objects, the mind is *determined* by custom to consider
its usual attendant, and to consider it in a stronger light upon
account of its relation to the first object.   'Tis this impression, then,
or *determination* which affords me the idea of necessity.'

And again[3] :

' All our reasonings concerning causes and effects are derived
from nothing but custom ; and belief is more properly an act of
the sensitive, than of the cogitative part of our natures.'[4]

Propensity, custom, force of habit, then, supply the connection between cause and effect.   How different is this from
Kant ?   For Kant, the category of causation is responsible for
the bond between cause and effect.   This category of causation is compelling, innate, absolute, inescapable.   It belongs
to the structure of our mind or understanding.   Thus Kant

---

[1] *Enquiries* (Selby-Bigge Edn.) (Oxford, 1902), pp. 43-44.
[2] *Treatise* (Selby-Bigge Edn.) (Oxford, 1897), pp. 155-156.
[3] *Ibid.* p. 183.
[4] It should be made clear that we are *not* defending Hume's doctrine as a doctrine
of causation.   What is valuable is his invocation of the force of custom as an
important element in the world, an element which cannot be disregarded by
philosophers.

has a *strong force* whereas Hume has a *gentle force* or propensity. Otherwise the Humian doctrine does not differ fundamentally from the Kantian, except that the latter is much wider, including other categories than that of cause and effect on which Hume had concentrated.

Note how like Kant is the following passage from Hume's *Treatise* :

Nothing is more curiously enquired after by the mind of man than the causes of every phaenomenon ; nor are we content with knowing the immediate causes, but push on our enquiries, till we arrive at the original and ultimate principle. We would not willingly stop before we are acquainted with that energy in the cause, by which it operates on its effect ; that tie which connects them together ; and that efficacious quality, on which the tie depends. This is our aim in all our studies and reflections : And how must we be disappointed, when we learn, that *this connection, tie, or energy lies merely in ourselves*, and is nothing but that determination of the mind, which is acquired by custom, and causes us to make a transition from an object to its usual attendant, and from the impression of one to the lively idea of the other ? Such a discovery not only cuts off all hope of ever attaining satisfaction, but even prevents our very wishes ; since it appears, that when we say we desire to know the ultimate and operating principle, as something, which resides in the external object, we either contradict ourselves, or talk without a meaning.[1]

With a few chiefly verbal alterations, such as substituting '*a priori*' for 'acquired by custom,' this passage could almost have been written by Kant. Even the attitude to metaphysics is much the same. Kant believes that metaphysics is impossible, while Hume here holds that the demand for knowledge having the character metaphysical is either contradictory or meaningless. Again in the *Enquiry*[2] he expresses the illusory character of metaphysical pursuits even more forcibly in the famous passage :

When we run over libraries, persuaded of these principles, what havoc must we make ? If we take in our hand any volume ; of divinity or school metaphysics, for instance ; let us ask, *Does it*

---

[1] *Treatise*, pp. 266–267.
[2] *Enquiries*, p. 165.

*contain any abstract reasoning concerning quantity or number?* No.
*Does it contain any experimental reasoning concerning matter of fact and
existence?* No. Commit it then to the flames : for it can contain
nothing but sophistry and illusion.

Kant, then, apart from his greater generality, is not nearly so
different from Hume as he imagined.

Kant, obedient to the dictates of the physical science of his
day,[1] makes *a priori* concepts rigid and necessary and innate.
Hume, on the other hand, with his social, political, and
historical pre-occupations, looks rather to custom, habit, and
the forces of society. In this of course the similarity to Lewis[2]
is quite obvious. Both build up the categorial structure on a
sociological basis : Lewis, like Kant, goes further afield than
Hume, since Hume devoted himself to the one relation of
cause and effect.[3]

The strength of society and 'nature' in Hume's philosophy
may be illustrated from a passage in the *Treatise*. Referring
to the difficulties into which pure reason led him, he writes :

Most fortunately it happens that since reason is incapable of
dispelling these clouds, nature herself suffices to that purpose,
and cures me of this philosophical melancholy and delirium, either
by relaxing this bent of mind, or by some avocation, and lively
impression of my senses, which obliterate all these chimeras. I
dine, I play a game of back-gammon, I converse, and am merry
with my friends ; and when after three or four hours' amusement, I
would return to these speculations, they appear so cold, and
strained, and ridiculous, that I cannot find in my heart to enter
into them further. . . . *I may, nay I must, yield to the current of
nature, in submitting to my senses and understanding* ; and in this blind
submission I show most perfectly my sceptical disposition and
principles.[4]

Hume thus shows himself to belong pre-eminently to what
in modern jargon would be called the ' sociological ' school,

[1] See p. 92.
[2] See pp. 101 f.
[3] In drawing attention to the similarity of the doctrines of Hume and Kant, an
important difference should not be overlooked. Hume's doctrine tends towards a
*passive* phenomenalism ; Kant's doctrine, and the Eddingtonian development of
that doctrine, lead to an *active* phenomenalism. This is a vital distinction.
(See Ch. XVIII).
[4] *Treatise*, p. 269.

and indeed to be a particularly illustrious member of that school. The increasing realization of this fact is no doubt responsible for the great revival of interest in Hume in recent years.

### The Categorial Philosophers

It may help in gaining a picture of the rise of categorial philosophy if we set out in the form of a table the salient features of the different philosophies discussed.

| Philosopher | Origin of the Categories |
|---|---|
| Hume | Gentle force of custom. |
| Kant | Compelling force, necessary, immutable, innate. |
| Wittgenstein | Linguistic sanction |
| Lewis | Pragmatic and sociological. |
| Poincaré | Conventional. |
| Eddington | Empirical success. |

It will be clear that Kant himself is off the main line of growth. His immense influence was retarding, in that it militated against the fluidity of the categories, and progressive, in that it brought out the salient features of the categorial situation much more clearly than Hume had done.

We can see clearly, too, how much philosophy is directed by the environment and preoccupations of the philosophers. We have pointed out how Hume was influenced by historical and social studies, and Kant by physical science and Rationalist metaphysics. Wittgenstein and Lewis reflect the ever-growing interest in recent times in linguistic and sociological topics.

Behind all these philosophers looms Protagoras: '*man is the measure.*'

Finally we must point out what is common to all the categorial philosophers from Kant to Eddington. They all believe there is only *one order*. They all believe that the world *must* be viewed categorially. Our contention is the negation of this. Throughout this work we are at pains to show that the world *may be, and indeed is*, viewed categorially in certain fields and for certain purposes. But we shall contend that we *can* know the world, in the manner of the *philosophia perennis* without superimposed categories ; and that in fact this is the way to the real order. There are two orders, the categorial and the real. The categorial philosophers have made a valuable contribution, but have vainly imagined that their doctrine was universal, and in this way have all but stultified it.

# CHAPTER VIII

# THE LOGIC OF THE CATEGORIAL

*The difference between man and the animals as evidenced in man's power of giving names, and thus making explicit classification of things, is a unique difference between the two.*

R. A. WILSON : *The Miraculous Birth of Language*

WE have already drawn attention to the distinction between the activities of the anatomist and the activities of the butcher. The one dissects out the natural structure of the animal. The other cleaves up the animal into convenient joints. We have interpreted modern physics by reference to this distinction. Now we will extend this theme of the two orders into wider realms, in particular into the manifold activities of human society.

A comparison of the traditional Aristotelean-Scholastic logic with some representative opinions in 'modern logic' will provide us with an entry into this field.

## Scholastic Logic and Modern Logic

According to the Scholastics, logic is the science which deals with the conceptual representation of the real order. It deals with things, not in themselves, but in thought. The real in itself, i.e. Being, is the object of metaphysics or ontology. Being is also the object of logic, not Being in itself, but in its conceptual representation. We know the real in or through the concept. In deductive reasoning we remain throughout on the conceptual plane. In inductive reasoning we rise from particulars in the real order up to the universal in the conceptual order.

This, in outline, is the structure of Scholastic logic.[1]

Let us now turn to some recent authors in the field of what we may designate ' modern logic ' (although the distinction between logic and metaphysics can hardly be applied to these works). Here we find a change of outlook amounting to a veritable Copernican revolution. There is no longer the appeal, as in Scholastic logic, to what we may call 'the structure of the universe,' or 'the nature of things,' but to something more like sociology.

For instance, in discussing necessary propositions, it is now commonly held by logicians that necessary propositions do not owe their necessity in any way to ' the structure of the universe.' Instead it is widely held that necessary propositions are really verbal, that they are rules of grammar, that they are about the use of words, that they record our determination to use words in a certain fashion, or that they arise from the proper conventional usage of language.[2]

According to this general school of thought the fact that, e.g., an object cannot be in two places at once is not due to the nature of things, which prevents this happening, but to the fact that our use of language forbids us to describe any situation whatever as that of an object being in two places at once. Whatever the state of affairs confronting us, the rules of English grammar forbid us saying that an object occupies two places at once. If a brick were at place A and a brick identical with the first in every respect were simultaneously at place B, then we *could* describe the situation either as a single brick in two places at once, or as two similar bricks in two different places. But the usage of the language requires the second account and forbids the first.

[1] On the subject of Scholastic logic, see e.g. Joyce, G. H. : *Principles of Logic* (London, 1902); Clarke, R. F. : *Logic* ; and Maritain, J. : *An Introduction to Logic* (London, 1937). It should be noted that Scholastic logic requires the distinction of the real and the conceptual orders. In the body of this work, however, where we are speaking of real in general, in opposing the real to the categorial orders, we do not explicitly mention this further distinction into real and conceptual in logic. This is merely for brevity and should cause no confusion.

[2] On this subject see an article by Norman Malcolm : ' *Are Necessary Propositions Really Verbal ?* ', *Mind*, 1940, p. 189.

' We find out necessary truths in the same way that we find out the empirical truth that if you suddenly jab a man with a pin he will jump,' says Norman Malcolm.[1] 'It is by observing the way people react in certain circumstances that we learn that a man will jump if you jab him with a pin ; and, likewise, it is by observing how people use expressions in certain circumstances that we learn necessary truths.'

The author goes on to describe how a child comes to learn the necessary truth : that A is larger than B entails B is smaller than A. The child learns this truth by noticing that people around him use 'A is larger than B' and 'B is smaller than A' interchangeably. It is simply by noticing this usage of language that we learn the necessary truth.[2]

Let us take another example. Is it possible for a surface to be both red and blue all over ? We give a negative reply to this. But why ? According to these logicians it is not because it is impossible to imagine a surface red and blue all over ; not because such a state of affairs is ruled out by 'the structure of the universe'; but because no state of affairs whatever is properly describable in English as 'red and blue all over.'

This school of thought maintains that the logical relations of a necessary proposition are, in fact, its meaning. *The meaning of a necessary proposition lies in its entailments, and the entailments are discovered by examining the customary and correct usage of language.* Malcolm writes[3] :

Philosophers and logicians have the idea that when a question as to whether one statement entails another arises, verbal considerations enter only because of ambiguity, and that the *real* question is not a verbal one, but one to be settled by the intellect's fixing its gaze upon the propositions *after* the ambiguity has been cleared up. But our point might be expressed like this : Clearing up the ambiguity of a statement *consists* in showing what it means,

---

[1] *Ibid.* p. 192.

[2] While the account of *how* the child learns is undoubtedly correct as far as it goes, the reader may differ from Malcolm on the question of precisely *what* it is that the child learns.

[3] *Ibid.* p. 197.

and this *consists* in showing how it is used, and this *consists* in showing what it entails.[1]

The foregoing remarks will serve to show something of the Copernican revolution in modern logic. Entailment has become a social function manifested in grammar and correct usage.

How different is the atmosphere from that of the traditional logic. Much of the discourse of the older logic is preserved, but now on a radically different basis. The new logic is *sociocentric*. The old logic is concerned with the representation of the real nature of the world. Our reason, according to the Scholastics, springs from the Divine Reason. Their logic is ultimately *theocentric*. Sociocentric *v.* theocentric is the contrast which gets to the root of the division between the two schools. Before examining these two schools further, we shall turn to a closer consideration of the legislative activity of society.

## The Legislative Activity of Society

It may make the subject clearer if we consider a hypothetical

[1] We cannot leave Malcolm's article without drawing attention to one revealing feature of his arguments. He concedes that the simple doctrine that necessity is verbal is only one side of the matter. He claims that it is nearer the mark to say that it is by observing how people use expressions in certain circumstances that we learn necessary truths. But there is one thing that he attacks vehemently. That is the notion that necessity is revealed by an act of the intellect, by an intuition, or by self-evidence. He is very firm that we do not see necessary connections ' by submitting them to the gaze of that wonderful faculty the intellect.' Now, on what is Malcolm basing this contention of his ? Is he saying that it is self-evident that if we look at the situation we shall see there is no such thing as self-evidence ? If so, and it is difficult to see what else he is saying, then his claim is self-refuting. He is basing his refutation on the very principle he believes he is refuting. He derides ' self-evidence ' on self-evident grounds. It would have been quite proper to criticise philosophers who invoke ' the gaze of that wonderful faculty, the intellect.' But Malcolm's mistake is to suppose that the only alternative is the linguistic theory of connections, nor does he see that his theory, proposed as a general theory, is self-refuting.

The basic principles on which Scholastic philosophy is erected are not to be seen in the gaze of the intellect in any literal sense. They are rather *inescapable companions.* That this is the case is usually overlooked by non-Scholastic philosophers who fail to distinguish the Scholastic Empiricism from Rationalism on the one hand (Descartes, Leibnitz, etc.) and simple Empiricism on the other (as in the English Empiricists).

case.[1]   Suppose that a bequest is made in a Will to the
Rationalist Society.   And suppose too that according to the
law charitable bequests are free from probate.   Is a bequest
to the Rationalist Society a charitable bequest or not?
How will the judge in a court of law set about deciding the
matter?

One school of thought would hold that to decide such a
matter we would first have to be clear on precisely what a
charitable bequest consisted of.   For this we would have to
look into the nature of 'charity.'   Then we would turn to a
consideration of the aims and objects of the Rationalist Society,
and determine whether they were such that the bequest was
or was not charitable.

But this sort of 'absolute' enquiry is not altogether what
the judge undertakes in practice.   Instead he looks out first for
precedents.   If a similar case has previously been decided upon
in court then our judge will be guided by it.   If there is no
precedent then he will weigh up the pros and cons.   Can the
aims of the Rationalist Society be described as charitable?
Its aims perhaps are humanitarian, but at the same time they
may or may not be directed to conventional morality.   They
are not likely to be directed to the furtherance of religion.
Furthermore, what does the Oxford Dictionary say about the
usage of the word 'charitable'?   How is the word used in
current speech?   In the common usage of the word today
would the aims of the Rationalist Society fall into the category
of charitable, whatever may have been the usage a century
ago?   What does current opinion say on the matter?   All
these factors the wise judge would have to ponder.

It appears then that *from the legal standpoint* to answer the
question: What is a charitable bequest? it is not possible
to give an answer by a cut and dried procedure.   It is not a
matter of looking inwards to the form of charitable bequests
as Plato might have held.   On the contrary, *the meaning of
the word or idea is not clear-cut and definite.   It has fuzzy edges.*

[1] For this example (although not the use made of it) I am inde_bted to Mr D.
Gasking.

The decision of the judge as to whether the Rationalist Society's aims fall within or without the area covered by the meaning of 'charity' is not a simple one. In giving his judicial decision the judge is creating both law and the meaning of words as much as interpreting them. He has to decide whether location at a certain point on the fuzzy edge is to be held henceforth to be inside or outside. *His decision extends the meaning of 'charity.' It throws as much light on 'charity' as on the Rationalist Society.*

We may appeal from our judge's decision. But eventually the decision of the highest court in the land is taken as normative.

The decision then is not 'absolute,' but 'social.' According to the sociological school of thought the answer to any question of the form : What is so and so ? will be of this kind.

From this point of view, What is a chair ? What is the State? What is justice ? and so on, are all questions to be answered by something like a judicial decision. It is society, exercising its legislative powers through language, and if necessary with the decision given through a court of law with its finger on society's pulse, to which we must turn for an answer to our problems.

Philosophical perplexity, according to these philosophers, arises from mistakenly imagining that there is one best insight or one true answer to any philosophical question. In fact, they say, such questions are many-sided, and there is no one side which is absolutely truer than any other.

Again, suppose someone is worried about how he can be certain that there is a table in front of him here and now, even though he has all the usual experiences of a table and no fear of hallucinations, conjurers, fairies, etc. This worry is a queer worry. For this man has no different expectations to everyone else who maintain that it is quite proper to say that there is a table in front of them now. In such a case the man should be guided by the ordinary rules of English which dictate that such a situation is to be described as 'there is a table in front of me now.'

As a final example we might take Bradley's contention that
relations between things are unintelligible.[1]  According to the
point of view here being expounded, in saying that one thing
cannot intelligibly be related to another Bradley is flagrantly
and wilfully misusing the term 'relation.'  It is for the King's
English to decide whether there are contradictions or not.
'Self-contradictory' and 'improper' go hand in hand.[2]

The reader cannot but be impressed by the cogency of many
of the arguments of the sociological school of thought.  There
is much truth in the contention e.g. that what constitutes by
convention a chair, as distinct from a stool or a couch, is of a
social and linguistic determination.  Even the case of 'charitable bequest,' we may concede, has *in practice* a strongly
'social' flavour.[3]

But on the other hand there are many features of the world
which must give us pause before embarking on a thoroughgoing
'social' logic.

Love, friendship, beauty, good.  These are things which
we know intensely, and we know that no language or social
convention or anything else can touch their inner core.  The
arguments of sociological philosophers become as dim and
distant as the sound of the waves to the Lotus eaters, when we
turn our minds to these mighty fortresses.

At a lower level too it is difficult to see, for instance, how the
discrete species in the animal and plant kingdoms are merely
sociological in their determination.  A horse is a horse and a
dog a dog : no amount of argument can reduce such hard
facts.  The situation here is quite different from that of a chair
and a stool, which undoubtedly merge into one another and

---

[1] *Appearance and Reality* (London, 1897), Ch. III.

[2] In the discussion of this section we have of course been treading on the
infinitely delicate ground of modern ' Cambridge ' philosophy.  This is a very
subtle and mobile school and it is unlikely that their thought has not in some
way been misrepresented here.  But if this is so it has not been wilful.  For a
survey of the modern Cambridge School and references to the important papers
see Farrell, B. A. : *Mind*, Jan. and April, 1946, *An Appraisal of Therapeutic Positivism.*

[3] It should be noted that we are not saying that in such cases there are no
forms or real natures.  We are merely conceding that in these cases discourse
may be, and often is, carried on without immediate reference to real natures.
This point will be discussed more fully in a later chapter (Ch. XVI).

are separable only sociologically. A horse and a dog are discrete and sharply separate, as are all the animal species, with only trivial exceptions.[1]

Reflections of this kind confirm our contention of the existence of two orders. In one Nature is at the helm. This is what we have called the *real order*. In the other the legislative power of society is determinative. This legislative power functions by allotting situations to conventional categories, categories which are usually implicit in current linguistic usage. This is what we have called the *categorial order*, or the order of *artifacts*.

With the object of further elucidating the distinction of the two orders, and yet their intimate interweaving, we will give another illustration.

A portrait in the ' modern ' manner by the artist Dobell was awarded a coveted prize for portraits at an art exhibition in Australia. A law-suit followed on the plea that the portrait was not really a portrait at all, but a caricature, and hence that the award was invalid. Now it should be noticed carefully what was the issue before the court. The issue was *not* whether the picture was or was not a good picture. The issue was: is this picture, or is it not, a portrait?

What is to be regarded at any given time as a portrait is plainly a social category. It is to be decided by the area of usage of the term ' portrait ' by the general consensus of educated people of the day. This is a sociological matter, and it may reasonably be held that it was quite rightly submitted to a court of law for a decision (cf. our previous discussion of the court's decision on what is a charitable bequest).

On the other hand the question: Is it a good picture? does not refer to a social category. It is not a question to be decided by a court of law. It is a question to be decided, if at all, by art critics who endeavour to reach down into the real order of values.

We can summarise the matter thus:

[1] In not discussing freaks and the possible fluidity of species in evolution, we do not really affect the present issue.

Is it a portrait ?—decided by judge in court of law, i.e. a social
category.
Is it a good picture ?—decided by art critics endeavouring to
reach out to real order.
It is the old contrast of *nomos* and *physis* over again.

The older logicians and philosophers of the *philosophia
perennis* were concerned primarily with the real order.  But in
recent times has come a renewed interest in society and its
functions, and in the logic of the categorial order which
society has created by subjecting the real to a categorial
transformation.

*These two schools of logicians are not necessarily antagonistic.
Instead they are properly complementary.*  Clashes only arise when
either school attempts to pass beyond its own proper bounds
into the territory of the other.

Let us now cast a backward glance to Immanuel Kant
who was the John the Baptist of modern categorial logic, as
he was too of the modern Procrustean interpretation of post-
Galilean physical science.

## Kant and the Transcendental Logic

We have already discussed the categorial philosophy of
Immanuel Kant in some detail (Ch. VI).  Kant, in the
course of his *Critique of Pure Reason*, propounded a logic
appropriate to his theory of the categorial.  This he calls
' Transcendental Logic.'  He writes[1] :

In the expectation, therefore, that there may perhaps be
concepts which relate *a priori* to objects, not as pure or sensible
intuitions, but solely as acts of pure thought—that is, as concepts
which are neither of empirical nor of aesthetic origin—we form for
ourselves by anticipation the idea of a science of the knowledge
which belongs to pure understanding and reason, whereby we think
objects entirely *a priori*.  Such a science, which should determine
the origin, the scope, and the objective validity of such knowledge,
would have to be called *transcendental logic*, because, unlike general
logic, which has to deal with both empirical and pure knowledge

---

[1] *Kritik*, B 81–2.  Kemp Smith's translation.

of reason, it concerns itself with the laws of understanding and of reason solely in so far as they relate *a priori* to objects.

In this passage replace 'acts of pure thought,' 'pure understanding,' 'reason,' etc., by 'conventional usage of language,' 'custom,' etc., and we have the modern logics of such philosophers as Moore, Malcolm and Lewy.

Hume was nearer the mark than Kant, as we have pointed out in Ch. VII, in that Hume appealed to custom, a gentle force, whereas Kant appealed to rigid and inescapable categories of the pure understanding for the transcendental logic. The looser version of Hume is much nearer the situation as envisaged today and much nearer the truth.

The one field in which Kant's rigidity is necessary (though of course not with the source from which Kant thought the rigidity sprang), is Procrustean physics. It is always the physical paradigm which is determinative with Kant. Hume, on the other hand, was more concerned with society, and his version of the transcendental logic is appropriate to the social categories.

Both Hume and Kant, and most of their successors, err by extending the transcendental, categorial, logic beyond its proper field to cover the whole universe. This is absurd, as we have seen. It comes from failure to recognise that there are in fact two orders : a real and a categorial. There is a logic of the real order and a logic of the categorial order. The older logicians concentrated on the real order. The more recent logicians represent a reaction from this. They concentrate exclusively on the categorial. The truth lies with both. There are two orders, and they are complementary.

Kant's categorial revolution was a mixture of success and failure. In this we may compare it with most new revolutionary intellectual movements. They are nearly all marked by excess, and it is left for subsequent generations to sift the wheat from the chaff. Consider the Marxist interpretation of history : violent, exaggerated, and ruthlessly intransigeant to the point of absurdity. Yet there is no doubt that it

contains something valuable in the germ.[1]  It has thrown
light in many dark corners.  For instance, the Marxists are
as yet the only people who have seriously attempted to give
any meaning and structure to the history of natural science,
which before their coming was left principally in the hands of
antiquarians.

The danger is always of carrying a good thing to excess,
and failing to preserve that balance for which the Greek
civilisation strove, although the Greeks did not always achieve
it.  David Hume was capable of giving very sound advice on
the subject, even if he did not always follow it himself.

The passion for philosophy, like that for religion, seems liable
to this inconvenience, that, though it aims at the correction of our
manners, and the extirpation of our vices, it may only serve, by
imprudent management, to foster a predominant inclination, and
push the mind, with more determined resolution, towards that side
which already *draws* too much, by the bias and propensity of the
natural temper.[2]

[1] See Ch. X.
[2] Hume : *Enquiries*, §. 34.

# CHAPTER IX

# MAN AS THE MEASURE

*Plato's Doctrine*

IS the world itself ordered, or does the mind impose order on the world ? This is the basic question. Kant drew forcible attention to the mind's power of imposing order. A modern Kantian, Lewis, is likewise decidedly in favour of this alternative : how we understand the world is by the categorial framed by the legislative activity of the mind directed pragmatically (Ch. VII). The whole modern sociological school of philosophy tends ultimately towards this second alternative.

Opposed to this notion that the only order in the world is that which is imposed by the mind, is the whole Plato-Aristotle-St. Thomas line of thought which holds that there are real natural kinds in the world, and that it is our business to discern them.

The real-kind doctrine is very strong in such cases as animal species, triangles, beauty, good, and so on. It is weaker with Plato's bed[1] where the infinite transition to sofa, couch, etc., must give us pause when a single form of a bed is proposed. Social legislation is obviously creeping in here. Plato himself in the *Parmenides*[2] was worried as to whether there really are forms of mud, hair, and such trivial things. And no wonder he was worried. These are well into the region which we treat as categorial, and it would be pedantic to insist on discussing objects like these in terms of their forms. In such cases as 'charitable bequest,' 'law' (as a subject of study in a University), and so on, the categorial activity of society is plainly uppermost, much in the manner in which Lewis describes it.[3]

[1] Plato : *Republic*, Bk. X.
[2] Plato : *Parmenides*, 130 c–e.
[3] See Chs. VII and VIII.

Where the arguments of the sociological philosophers are strongest is where Plato's theory of forms is least illuminating. But where the theory of forms is strongest is just where we must acknowledge that our own legislative activities are feeblest. We feel a compelling power in good, beauty, etc., which no social convention can reach.[1]

For the present let us say that it is for the most part the greatest and wisest men, the educated men, the influential men, who lead society in making definitions and normalising usages, and who are thus legislators in the realm of the categorial. But just as man's control stops at the shore, so when they come up hard against objective reality (real forms, to use Platonic terminology) their control stops.

To show how Plato's mind was working along somewhat the same lines, let us revert to the passage in the *Parmenides* previously referred to :

Are you also puzzled, Socrates, about cases that might be thought absurd, such as hair or mud or dirt or any other trivial and undignified objects ? Are you doubtful whether or not to assert that each of these has a separate Form distinct from things like those we handle ?

Not at all, said Socrates ; in these cases, the things are just the things we see ; it would surely be too absurd to suppose that they have a Form. All the same, I have sometimes been troubled by a doubt whether what is true in one case may not be true in all. Then, when I have reached that point, I am driven to retreat for fear of tumbling into a bottomless pit of nonsense. Anyhow, I get back to the things which we were just now speaking of as having Forms, and occupy my time with thinking about them (i.e. Rightness, Beauty, Goodness and all such things).[2]

It is fairly clear that Plato is feeling his way here to a recognition of two orders. The theory of forms, of real kinds, is

---

[1] The compelling power of beauty is strikingly shown in the aesthetic conversions which sometimes occur in a manner similar to religious conversions. Here is an instance : Most of the early immigrants to Australia on their arrival could see nothing beautiful in the Australian landscape. To them the Bush was gloomy and melancholy. Such was the experience of the artist Tom Roberts during his earlier years in Australia. But one day when walking near the Yarra river it suddenly came upon him that the landscape was beautiful, and he felt its beauty for the rest of his days. He had gone through a sudden aesthetic re-orientation.

[2] *Parmenides*, 130 (Cornford's translation).

applicable to the real order only. When the trivial or conventional character of things captures our thoughts, then is the time to turn to good and beauty and the rest of the great realities to realise that there is another aspect of the world.

It is always so through the ages. When we hear the insinuating whisper of Protagoras 'man is the measure of all things,' let us say : 'yea, up to a point, but beyond that point we cannot go.'

Here again are the words of Plato, this time in the *Cratylus*.[1]

*Socrates*. But would you say, Hermogenes, that the things differ as the names differ ? and are they relative to individuals, as Protagoras tells us ? For he says that man is the measure of all things, and that things are to me as they appear to me, and that they are to you as they appear to you. Do you agree with him, or would you say that things have a permanent essence of their own ?

*Hermogenes*. There have been times, Socrates, when I have been driven in my perplexity to take refuge with Protagoras ; not that I agree with him at all.

*Socrates*. What ! have you even been driven to admit that there was no such thing as a bad man ?

*Hermogenes*. No, indeed ; but I have often had reason to think that there are very bad men, and a good many of them.

*Socrates*. Well, and have you ever found any very good ones ?

*Hermogenes*. Not many.

*Socrates*. Still you have found them ?

*Hermogenes*. Yes.

*Socrates*. And would you hold that the very good were the very wise, and the very evil very foolish ? Would that be your view ?

*Hermogenes*. It would.

*Socrates*. But if Protagoras is right, and the truth is that things are as they appear to anyone, how can some of us be wise and some of us foolish ?

*Hermogenes*. Impossible.

*Socraess*. And if, on the other hand, wisdom and folly are really distinguishable, you will allow, I think, that the assertion of Protagoras can hardly be correct. For if what appears to each man is true to him, one man cannot in reality be wiser than another.

*Hermogenes*. He cannot.

[1] *Cratylus*, 385 f. (Jowett's translation).

*Socrates.* Nor will you be disposed to say with Euthydemus, that all things equally belong to all men at the same moment and always ; for neither on his view can there be some good and other bad, if virtue and vice are always equally to be attributed to all.

*Hermogenes.* There cannot.

*Socrates.* But if neither is right, and things are not relative to individuals, and all things do not equally belong to all at the same moment and always, they must be supposed to have their own proper and permanent essence : they are not in relation to us, or influenced by us, fluctuating according to our fancy, but they are independent, and maintain to their own essence the relation prescribed by nature.

*Hermogenes.* I think, Socrates, that you have said the truth.

Let us make the position clear. We are not saying, whatever Plato might have believed, that the trivial or conventional has no real nature. On the contrary, every object must have some real nature, some ground which makes it what it is. But what we are asserting is that in some regions—broadly those far down towards the bottom of Plato's divided line, it is not always appropriate to consider things in terms of real natures. For practical purposes it is often more convenient to abstract from the real natures and consider things according to some more arbitrary grouping. This leads us into the categorial order, which is superimposed, as it were, on the real order and often cuts across the latter. We will discuss this in more detail in a later chapter on St. Thomas and his logic.[1]

## The Sophists

The sophists were largely concerned to draw attention to the categorial in the form of social conventions, usages of language, etc. This is at least one interpretation of the famous dictum of Protagoras, that 'man is the measure of all things.' The dictum is true enough in the categorial order although not true in the real order. But the sophists, like so many philosophers after them, drove their notions to excess. Not content with pointing out the important rôle played by habit, custom, and convention, they, or some of them, went to extremes

[1] Ch. XVI.

and maintained that *all* things were governed in this way. This well nigh universal tendency to excess may perhaps be attributed to the pride which bids us cling to our ideas, however artificial the situation thereby becomes. To say that *some* things are *nomos* is salutary. To insist that *all* is *nomos*, and *nothing* is *physis*, is wilful pride.

It was when the sophists overlapped into the domain of the real that Socrates rightly pulled them up, as e.g. when it was maintained by Thrasymachus that Justice is merely the name given by society to the advantage of the stronger.

Plato is so concerned with the refutation of the sophists in the domain of the real that he does not deal as he might have with the genuine aspect of their teaching about society and the categorial aspect of the world.

The sophists, the Kantians, the modern sociological logicians, sin by commission, by going too wide. The Platonists, the Thomists, tend to sin by omission in not adequately discussing the important aspect of the world which the other school has fastened on to.

## Words and Things

In the categorial order we cannot effect a clean separation between things and words, as we can in the real order. In the categorial order what a 'thing' is depends in part on the breadth of the linguistic category. The man who insists 'I don't care what you call it, I am concerned with what it is' is making a demand applicable to the world of real kinds in a region where we categorise. It is thus an illicit and anti-social demand, though perhaps natural enough at first sight.

We can translate this matter into terms of connotation and denotation. These are clear and distinct in the traditional logic, which is the logic of the real. But in the logic of the categorial the distinction between the two fades, and they become intimately interwoven.

CONNOTATION (or Intension) refers to the characteristics making up a concept which covers a number of individuals, e.g. dog, while the individuals so covered constitute the DENOTATION (or Extension).

Now in the categorial logic, e.g. that arising from linguistic usage, we have it in our power to alter the denotation (as in our example of the charitable bequest (p. 118)), and by so doing we alter the connotation. It is through the denotation that we arrive at the connotation in this realm. In fact, in a sense, in the categorial logic the denotation and the connotation are the same thing.[1] This of course is quite different from the situation in the logic of the real where we are dealing with real natures, e.g. the nature of a dog. There the connotation and the denotation are quite separate and distinct. To use Socrates' phrase, the proper and permanent essence is not in relation to us or influenced by us. Likewise, it does not fluctuate with the denotation.

To take up the matter from another angle, if we take a term in common use it is often a matter of debate whether or not a real nature is enshrined within it at the core. For instance in the mists of the term 'State' is there, or is there not, a real nature? Some people might be inclined to say No! Others, like Hegel and Plato, would maintain that there is a real nature on which the conventional usage of the word sits lightly.

Or, to put the matter in yet another way, important words are often used very widely and vaguely, and yet may also have 'strict' senses. E.g. the word 'good.' 'Good' in ordinary speech is very wide, and even nebulous. Yet many moral philosophers (including of course those of the *philosophia perennis*) believe that there is also a specifically ethical use of the word. The first use, i.e. the wide colloquial use, is categorial in that it depends on the prevailing customs of language. The 'strict' use is the use of the word when it refers to the real nature.

## *Man the Measure in Common Life*

We tend to overlook the wide ramifications of man as the measure. A characteristic letter of G. K. Chesterton brings it home to us very forcibly [2]:

[1] cf. pp. 119 f.
[2] Letter to his future wife, Sept. 29th, 1899. Quoted in the Biography by Maisie Ward (London, 1944), pp. 102 f.

. . . as to what I do every day : it depends on which way you want it narrated : what we all say it is, or what it really is.

What we all say happens every day is this : I wake up : dress myself, eat bacon and bread and coffee for breakfast : walk up to High Street Station, take a fourpenny ticket for Blackfriars. . . .

This is what we, in our dreamy, deluded way, really imagine is the thing that happens. What really happens (but hist ! are we observed ?) is as follows.

Out of the starless night of the Uncreated, that was before the stars, a soul begins to grope back to light. It gropes its way through strange, half-lighted chambers of Dreams . . . till the soul in one last struggle, plunges into a body, as into a house, and wakes up within it. Then he rises . . . He goes through a number of extraordinary and fantastic rituals ; which the pompous elf-land he has entered demands. . . .

He takes a sword in his hand (for what may not befall him in so strange a country !) and goes forth : he finds a hole in the wall, a little cave wherein sits One who can give him the charm that rules the horse of water and fire. . . .

Chesterton continues in this half whimsical, half serious vein, and adds :

This is not all so irrelevant as you may think. It was this line of feeling that taught me, an utter Rationalist so far as dogma goes, the lesson of the entire Spirituality of things—an opinion that nothing has ever shattered since. I can't express myself on the point, nobody can. But it is *only* the spirituality of things that we are sure of. . . .

For Chesterton there is a real world, the world of spirit, and there is a very extensive world of what we would call conventional artifacts, which in daily life are overlaid on the real world and obscure it to a greater or lesser extent.

It is the function of Art to shock us out of this artificial world and to make us more vividly aware of the real world ever present behind. Most of us experience sometimes, for shorter or longer intervals, the sensation of the blinkers being off, and the world suddenly coming to new life : thus felt for instance Pippa in Browning's poem :

*The year's at the spring,*
*And day's at the morn ;*
*Morning's at seven ;*
*The hill-side's dew-pearled ;*
*The lark's on the wing ;*
*The snail's on the thorn :*
*God's in His heaven—*
*All's right with the world !*

Carlyle and Hopkins, to whom we have already appealed, witness to the same truth in their different ways.

For the daily round Protagoras takes us by the hand. But his is no abiding city. We must turn our steps towards the real city if we are to find a home.[1]

Sometimes this rising up to a higher level comes apparently spontaneously. More often it is the response to the sublime in Nature, or it comes at the sudden quickening of Art : the wind-swept moors, the sunlit plains and the everlasting hills, 'Toledo in a Storm,' 'Augustus as Pontifex Maximus,' 'The Eroica,' 'The Grammarian's Funeral' : they all snatch us up from the world of Protagoras.

We hunger and thirst for Art in common life because there it is a fountain of Life. 'Art is that which is reborn of the Spirit,' says Hegel, and it has in it the power to raise other spirits powerfully above. By Art we ascend to the heights of the natural world. To transcend the natural order and reach the supernatural plane we must follow the Mystics in the ascent of Mount Carmel.

[1] cf. Samuel Butler's *Erewhon* and the conquest of the machines over man. Similarly we are in danger that our mental artifacts will come to overwhelm us.

# CHAPTER X

# PROCRUSTES AT LARGE

*General*

PROCRUSTES is a good servant but a bad master. When he is employed with full realisation of what is taking place his activities may be beneficent. Modern Procrustean physics is a notable instance of this harnessing of Procrustes to achieve a desired goal. But when he is active without our realising it, then there is a danger that he will become a tyrant, and even a raging tyrant.

We can find Procrustes at work at almost every turn, sometimes for good and sometimes for evil.

When we insist '*always* some trickery in haunted houses,' we are employing a Procrustean bed. Similarly when we say 'water divining must be a deception,' 'miracles can't happen,' 'astrology must be wrong,' 'there is no such thing as magic,' 'communists are always wicked/good' (according to taste), we are invoking Procrustes. The old adage about giving a dog a bad name is long standing recognition of this subtle process. When we divide society into rigid income tax groups, or trade groups, when chemists divide matter rigidly into organic and inorganic, or into metals and non-metals, when we discuss art rigidly in terms of schools of art, we are passing from a rough and ready basis in the real world into the rigidity of a Procrustean world. The reader will, no doubt, be able to think of multitudes of other examples.

The following dialogue, culled from the pages of *Punch*, shows how an ingenious and resourceful man can uphold a thesis by being sufficiently ruthless about it. This is an instance of the Procrustean bed *par excellence*, and may serve as a model of much that goes on in the name of philosophy.[1]

I met a man about a week ago who took a very firm line about badgers.   He said they didn't exist.   'Somehow or other,' he said, 'the idea has grown up that the people wish to be told stories about this preposterous animal, and letters are written to *The Times* and to *Country Life* about it.   But there aren't any.   If there were, I should have seen one—and I haven't.'

I said I had.

'Where ? '

'In a wood.'

'Pure hallucination.   A lot of people have told me that they have seen ghosts.   But I don't believe it.   I've seen none myself. What was this thing doing ? '

'Moving about.'

'Was it eating anything ? '

'Not that I noticed.'

'Did it emit any groans ? '

'No.'

'Did it carry its head in its hand ? '

I was thoroughly annoyed.   'One of my earliest recollections,' I said, 'is that of being taken to see a live badger in a cage.   It was in Leicestershire.   It was kept by a clergyman.   His name was Twigg.'

'How do you know he was a clergyman ? '

'How do I what ?   Well he wore black clothes and a dog-collar.'

'Just as I thought.   It was probably a disguise.'

'There were badgers,' I said, 'in Ken Wood at Hampstead quite recently.   They came into people's gardens.'

'Did you see them there ? '

'They came at night, and left their traces.'

'You're sure you don't mean burglars ? '

'Look here,' I said.   'There is a badger at the Zoo.'

'Probably a small Panda.'

'How do you know there is a Panda at the Zoo ? '

'I've seen it.'

'How do you know it wasn't a large badger ? '

'Because there aren't any badgers.'

[1] ' *The Unbeliever*,' by Evoe.   *Punch*, May 17th, 1944.

'When I tell you that I know farmers who give a guinea a year to badger-digging parties, because they say the badgers eat their young lambs, when I say that you can see the traces of badgers at any time in hundreds of places, when I assure you that books have been written about the lives and loves of badgers, photographs reproduced of badgers and their young—'

'Ectoplasm,' he said.

'Badgers make admirable pets. There are people writing to the papers who honour and cherish them. These people sit down to tea with their badgers and drink milk with them. Badgers are very tidy. They live in setts, and are drawn by dogs—'

'Like the Eskimos.'

'They are plantigrades. They bring out their beds to be aired. They are obstinate. They bite. They eat roots, beetles, worms, rabbits. The shriek of a badger at night is a very terrible thing.'

'So is the shriek of a ghost.'

'Probably many of the stories about ghosts originate from the cry of a badger.'

'You might just as well say that many of the stories about badgers originate from the cry of a ghost.'

'Possibly the trolls and gnomes were badgers.'

'Possibly the badgers were gnolls and tromes.'

'Badger-baiting was one of the most popular sports of our ancestors.'

'So was killing dragons.'

'What do you *really* believe about badgers ? '

'In an excessively urbanized country it is found necessary to invent stories of glamour and mystery about the countryside, and the wild creatures of the woods. Badgers is one of them.'

'Are one of them.'

'Is one of them. There may have been badgers long ago, just as there were dragons and griffins. But they are gone.'

\*　　　\*　　　\*

'Do you deny then the whole testimony of Natural History books, encyclopaedias and zoologists ? '

'Paid propaganda.'

The man was becoming tiresome.

\*　　　\*　　　\*

The amusing character of this argument should not blind the reader to the moral which may be drawn from it.

A philosopher will often start off well by making out the real nature of some part of the world in which he has been interested. But only too often he will proceed by Procrustean-ising more and more in an endeavour to bring everything into his net. So many theories trail off into arid wastes in the endeavour to achieve a premature unity. It is often difficult to determine precisely where one process leaves off and the other begins. Philosophers themselves are usually very vague about it.

It should be borne in mind that if the exponent of some philosophy is sufficiently determined, and is prepared to use *ad hoc* hypotheses at every turn, then there is often no way to unseat him by producing facts, although the critic can make it very uncomfortable for him. For when facts are produced he will assimilate them, if he is sufficiently ruthless, however much out of joint this may put things. It is only in time that the absurdity becomes manifest. For his *ad hoc* structure will eventually become so elaborate and artificial that its falsity will be plainly visible to all. So in the long run even very well concealed Procrustean beds are in vain, but in the mean-while they can be very deceptive, and indeed may deceive even the very elect.

Hence the necessity of searching for them diligently. It is our contention that concealed Procrustean beds are at the bottom of a great many, if not all, modern philosophies, and it is by their means that these philosophies acquire whatever speciousness they possess.

Let us consider a few examples from modern philosophical, historical, and scientific systems.

### Hedonism

The naïve exponent of hedonism will insist that we all *do in fact* pursue pleasure, and that this is the driving force of life. By a confusion he will sometimes say that we all *should* pursue pleasure, though why it is necessary to make this ethical recommendation if we all *do* follow pleasure in any case, is not clear.

To maintain psychological hedonism the hedonist philosopher will need to go to great lengths. Even the martyr at the stake must be said to be pursuing pleasure. The pleasure he gets from martyrdom exceeds the pangs of the flames.

This is the sort of artificial position the hedonist must defend when he brings out his Procrustean bed and insists on filling it. Its artificiality is so transparent in extreme cases like the martyr that one wonders how anyone could be found to uphold it. But there are such people.

The valid starting-point of psychological hedonism is that some people do frequently pursue pleasure, and probably all people do at some time. The rest is Procrustean.

## Behaviourism

The behaviourists reduce psychology to physiological reactions in the body. This once-popular doctrine is supported by experiments showing correlations between psychical events and bodily nervous events. The behaviourists then deny the reality of the psychical events and maintain that there are only the bodily events. It is a very naïve materialist system and is overthrown at the first touch of criticism, e.g. that we know material happenings by means of our mental faculty. If the latter did not exist we could never know the former. It is ridiculous to identify the mental and the material. They are incommensurable.

Yet the behaviourists, by a combination of blindness and ingenuity, go on maintaining their doctrines. Whatever psychical event is suggested they find some physiological process and identify it with that. In other words, they are determined operators of a Procrustean bed which reduces everything to physiology.

## Logical Positivism

This is a modern expression of an old tendency in philosophy, as old in fact as philosophy itself.

Logical positivism was at its height ten or twenty years ago. Today it is rarely found in its naïve form, except perhaps in the United States of America. Although logical positivism as such is practically dead today, we shall discuss it at some length because it is implicit in the background of many more sophisticated philosophies. And, too, because of its relative simplicity, its character is clear ; a character which we will find is largely Procrustes in disguise.

The movement has centred around the 'Vienna circle' and the closely related school in Cambridge associated with such names as Bertrand Russell and Wittgenstein.[1] At Oxford it had an enthusiastic adherent in A. J. Ayer, whose work *Language Truth and Logic* is a straightforward and readable exposition of logical positivism.

The central doctrine of logical positivism is '*a proposition has no meaning unless it can be empirically verified*' or '*the meaning of a proposition is its method of verification.*'

The acceptance of this principle means first of all the elimination of metaphysics. For the propositions of metaphysics are not of the kind susceptible of empirical verification. Consequently the logical positivist dismisses them as meaningless. This goes further than did Kant, who held, amongst other arguments, that we could not, in fact, pursue metaphysics because the mind became lost in insoluble contradictions when it ventured out beyond possible experience. The logical positivist holds that the propositions of metaphysics are inherently meaningless. Thus Ayer writes :

Our charge against the metaphysician is not that he attempts to employ the understanding in a field where it cannot profitably venture, but that he produces sentences which fail to conform to the conditions under which alone a sentence can be literally significant.[2]

This disposes of metaphysics, which is seen to be nonsense. In fact the term ' metaphysical ' has come to be used as a term of contempt and even abuse.

[1] It should be noted that the ' Cambridge school ' today has progressed far from logical positivism. It has become much more pliable and subtle. But its positivist ancestry persists in intruding itself.

[2] Ayer, A. J. : *Language, Truth and Logic*, p. 19.

As regards the propositions of formal logic and mathematics there is a *prima facie* difficulty. For these appear to have a necessity and certainty quite beyond any empirical proposition. They can scarcely be dismissed as easily as the propositions of metaphysics on the ground that they are nonsense. But they must be accounted for in some way. John Stuart Mill held that their certainty differs from that of ordinary empirical propositions only in degree. He believed them to be inductive generalisations based on such an immense number of instances that their probability amounted practically to certainty.

The logical positivists, however, reject this theory of Mill's. They hold that the propositions of logic and mathematics are universally sure and certain because they are *tautologies* or *analytic propositions*. In other words, they are true universally simply because we never allow them to be untrue. The reader will notice the similarity here to our contention in Ch. III that the laws of physics are always true simply because we never allow them to be violated.[1] But whereas the laws of physics are alterable by the consent of the body of physicists, the principles of logic and mathematics acquire a higher universality and permanence by being dictated by the set rules of language. All necessary propositions are analytic propositions or tautologies, and record our determination to use words in a certain fashion. They are entirely devoid of factual content, and hence comes their certainty.[2]

On turning to the realm of ethics and aesthetics, the logical positivists are obliged to propound a radical theory. The propositions of ethics and aesthetics are clearly not capable of empirical verification, at least not in the ordinary sense of the term ; e.g. the proposition that a certain act is a good act, or that a certain picture is good or beautiful. A strict adherence to the criterion that meaning resides in verifiability would make it necessary to rule out all such statements as

---

[1] It should be noted that logical positivists have not generally turned their attention to the Procrustean theory of physics. An exception is Wittgenstein, who, in the *Tractatus Logico-Philosophicus*, holds one form of the Procrustean theory (See Ch. VII).

[2] On this subject see Ayer, *op. cit.* Ch. IV.

inherently meaningless. Logical positivists are not prepared to go to such lengths. They escape from the dilemma by denying that statements of value are statements of fact at all, or that they are literally significant. They maintain that, on the contrary, they are: 'simply expressions of emotion which can be neither true nor false.'[1]

And again:

The exhortations to moral virtue are not propositions at all, but ejaculations or commands which are designed to provoke the reader to action of a certain sort.[2]

The person making the statement of value is, ostensibly at least, expressing his own emotion by his language, and is endeavouring to induce others to have similar feelings.

This theory means that we do not express our own feelings, and endeavour to lead others to feel likewise, *because* we consider the picture to be beautiful, or the act right, or whatever the case may be. Instead, the logical positivists would have us believe, we persuade others when we have no objective judgment of fact, but merely our own arbitrary fancy which we are endeavouring to impress on others. Apparently, for the logical positivist, we are completely ego-centric.

A more mature version of this theory of ethics and aesthetics has recently been published in a comprehensive work by C. L. Stevenson, in which he links it up with pragmatism.[3] Stevenson traces the evolution of this general approach to ethics, from the Greek sophists, through David Hume, up to the present day. He is at pains to make clear that this theory of ethics as persuasion does not necessarily mean egotistical caprice or dogmatism, nor does it end in general scepticism. For, he believes, persuasive methods should be based on the fullest knowledge of scientific facts, and if based on such superior knowledge the persuasion of others is justified and will lead people eventually to be thankful for guidance. Stevenson writes[4]:

[1] *Ibid.* p. 150.
[2] *Ibid.* p. 151.
[3] Stevenson, C. L. : *Ethics and Language* (Yale University Press, 1945).
[4] *Ibid.* p. 332.

Although the effect of beliefs on attitudes is ever present, it is often slow. Our writer may find that there is a prolonged lag between his readers' acceptance of his reasons and their subsequent emotional readjustment. Old ways are not easily unlearned, and persist long after they are acknowledged to have outlived their function. Now here is a place where persuasive methods, cautiously used, have a legitimacy that is scarcely open to question. If our writer's persuasion does not supplant his reasons, but simply hastens their effect, it will come as a welcome aid.

Stevenson is what we might call a ' *descendentalist* ' as opposed to a ' *transcendentalist* ' like Plato. He deplores the age-old quest for ultimate definitive principles, which

not only hides the full complexity of moral issues, but puts static, other-worldly norms in the place of flexible, realistic ones.[1]

Where Ayer would say that ethical terms are imperatives, Stevenson is more subtle. He looks rather to a psychological emotive meaning:

The emotive meaning of a word is the power that the word acquires, on account of its history in emotional situations, to evoke or directly express attitudes, as distinct from describing or designating them[2].

He does not tell us *how* and *why* the word comes to acquire this power however.

This persuasive guidance effected by the use of ethical terms is to be done by clear-minded and factually enlightened men. Stevenson anticipates that:

the growth of empirical knowledge will slowly lead to a world of enlightened moral accord.[3]

Enough has been said to show the character of a well-developed 'humanistic' theory of morals. It is the culmination of the movement stemming from Protagoras : man is the measure of all things. We have discussed this subject of ethics at some length because of its intrinsic importance. Such humanistic doctrines are very widely held today in some form or another.

We will now go on to show that this elaborate structure

[1] *Ibid.* p. 336.
[2] *Ibid.* p. 33.
[3] *Ibid.* p. 136.

is built upon sand. Its foundation is a concealed Procrustean bed, and when this is brought to light the whole structure collapses.

## Critique of Logical Positivism

Let us turn back to the starting point of logical positivism, to the foundation on which all this structure rests. This is the principle that '*a proposition has no meaning unless it can be empirically verified.*' (In the light of Stevenson's emendations this is now to be understood as 'no *factual* meaning.' The proposition may yet have an *emotive* meaning, to use Stevenson's own language).

Now when any general proposition is put forward, a good plan is to apply it to itself and observe the result. In so many cases when this is done the proposed principle shows itself to be self-contradictory, as for example : 'Everything is doubtful.' On its own criterion this is doubtful, so that *universal scepticism cannot be asserted without denying itself* (cf. Descartes). (It should be noted that the principles of the *philosophia perennis* do *not* annihilate themselves in this way. On the contrary, they assert themselves in the very act of being denied, so that far from being inherently self-contradictory, they are inherently self-assertive).

When we introvert the basic principle of logical positivism we find it to be a proposition which is inherently self-contradictory. For such a proposition as 'a proposition has no meaning unless it can be empirically verified' is not itself susceptible of empirical verification, and therefore, by its own criterion, it is meaningless.

*All the logical positivist is doing is to express his private determination to admit only empirically verifiable propositions.* No reason is given for this. It is evidently founded on nothing more substantial than prejudice and emotion. The basic proposition in fact, in Stevenson's own phrase, has only an emotive meaning. Its purpose is to persuade subtly to pursue a certain line of thought.

Various motives might be suggested for this line of persuasion.[1]

The basic proposition is closely akin to one aspect of the discipline of the experimental sciences.[2] Logical positivism is in some measure in harmony with the procedure of these sciences. We might reasonably conclude that, dazzled by the success of the sciences, these philosophers have hypostatised what they suppose is the scientific procedure and have put it forward as a proposition true of the world in general.

Another motive that might be suggested is that such a system as logical positivism might seem to offer an escape from the supposed tyranny of absolute morals.[3] It is possible that some embrace it for this reason.

Others again may be impelled by theophobia. Since logical positivism denies anything transcendental it clears away at least natural theology, and probably mystical theology as well.[4]

Whatever the motive or motives may be, and they probably vary from one exponent to another, the result is the same. It is the annihilation of metaphysics, and the devitalising of morals and art. Ayer leaves individuals as egotists imposing their arbitrary wills on others. Stevenson, more guarded, develops the pernicious dichotomy between facts and emotions and regards morals as mass persuasion. But what does this

[1] Notice that first we considered the truth or falsity of the doctrine in itself. Having decided it is false we can now go on and ask the further question. Why are these false doctrines proposed? Failure to consider the rational foundation *first* is one of the philosophic vices of our age. To launch into a psychological account of influences and origins without having previously settled the question of truth or falsity, inevitably leads to a doctrine of general relativism, and ultimately to futility.

Examine the rational foundations of a system first. If it is in error, then we can go on to ask the further question : Why did the author err? The answering of this question is the proper place for an examination of influences on the author, which may well lead us to an understanding of his aberrations. But, no matter how illuminating it may be, an enquiry into origins, in itself, can never give us the answer to the primary question. Is it true or false?

[2] With the exception of Wittgenstein (Ch. VII), the logical positivists assume a passive phenomenalism. (See Ch. XVIII).

[3] In point of fact it is more likely to throw us into the arms of the much worse tyranny of absolute convention.

[4] See Ayer, *op. cit.* pp. 180 f.

amount to but mass conditioning? It is taking over the
technique of modern American advertising.. Stevenson's
moral theory is somewhat reminiscent of Plato's 'noble lie,'[1]
but with the all-important difference that it lacks the absolute
ethical foundations on which Plato bases it. In Stevenson's
hands it is a cold-blooded and dangerous doctrine. Antigone's
cry is as much in protest against the Stevensons as against
State tyranny. The fact that Stevenson stipulates that the
conditioning must be done by clear-minded well-informed
men does not save the situation. For who are the clear-
minded and informed men? The dominant intellectual
class in each age would assume this position in the absence of
absolute standards. And who is more tyrannical than the
convinced humanist intellectual, for all his professions to the
contrary? Alternatively, having been carefully conditioned,
we would be like contented pigs lolling in clover (cf. Aldous
Huxley's *Brave New World*).

The logical positivist starts with an observation about the
empirical sciences : that empirical verifiability is part of the
criterion of truth in those sciences. Then he makes the mistake
of endeavouring to squeeze all the rest of the world into the
same pattern. This, in other words, means that he is employing a Procrustean bed. But he seems to be unconscious of it,
although it is clear enough when pointed out. Procrustes,
unrecognised, has become a raging tyrant. In effect then,
the Viennese and Cambridge men, under the obsession of
modern science, or for some other reason, have shut themselves up in a prison house of their own making. It is a
characteristic of the neurotic that on the subject of his
neurosis he is not free. He fences himself in, and it becomes a
blind spot on his rational life. Would it be too much to say
that this is the case with the logical positivists, that they are
suffering from a mass neurosis?

To quote the words of a reviewer of Ayer's work[2] :

'Under the pretence of ultimate wisdom it guillotines religion,

[1] Plato : *Republic* 414 f.
[2] Quoted by Stevenson, *op. cit.* p. 265.

ethics and aesthetics, self, persons, free will, responsibility and everything worth while. I thank Mr Ayer for having shown us how modern philosophers can fiddle and play tricks while the world burns.'

The logical positivist structure is founded upon a concealed Procrustean bed. That its exponents have not detected the nature of its foundation may be simply because, in their enthusiasm, they have never stopped to examine the foundation. But that they should resist all attempts at enlightenment is a mystery which only the psycho-therapists can unravel. However this is a common enough phenomenon in many fields, to some others of which we must now turn.

## *The Materialist Interpretation of History*

According to the so-called 'materialist' interpretation of history, associated principally with the name of Karl Marx, it is the economic structure of society which directs history. It alone is ultimately causal, all else in civilisation is epiphenomenal. Consequently to achieve a real insight into history we must pursue economic history. Great world events are not due primarily to statesmen, philosophers, prophets, soldiers, great men, and so on. They are fundamentally economic in origin.

There is no doubt that there is much truth in this contention. In view of the steady preoccupation of the great mass of mankind in food, shelter, and clothing, it may readily be admitted that the economic force is a potent one in history and has often been underestimated. The potency of this force is no new discovery : it has been recognised from time to time at least since the days of Thucydides and Plato. But the Marxist contention that the economic factor is the *only* real causal factor is giving it an exaggerated importance which cannot be sustained.[1] Yet the exponent of Marxist theory is wedded to it as a basic principle. He *must* show that

[1] cf. Thomas Carlyle : ' It is not to taste sweet things, but to do noble and true things, and vindicate himself under God's Heaven as a god-made Man, that the poorest son of Adam dimly longs. Show him the way of doing that, the dullest daydrudge kindles into a hero.'—*On Heroes and Hero-worship*. Which has the more profound insight into human nature, Carlyle or Marx ?

world events are accounted for economically. *When history fails him he slides insensibly into a Procrustean bed.*

It is but a little step from reading economic causes *in* history to reading them *into* history. There is a given historical event X to be explained. The objective historian will seek out all the influences, economic and otherwise, which throw light on X. But the Marxist historian will select out the economic facts, and if they are meagre will not hesitate to magnify them to larger proportions, like Procrustes of old, until the Procrustean bed having been made, he will come forward with the triumphant conclusion that he has given an economic explanation to event X.

It is fatally easy for the doctrinaire Marxist to slip into the Procrustean technique and thereby produce a sham history to support the Marxist theory. Just where objective history stops and sham Procrustean history starts is a matter for the informed and judicious critic to decide. But although we cannot easily draw the dividing line, the fact that there is a dividing line is clear enough.

To take a contemporary example, let us consider the rise of the Fascist and National Socialist movements in Italy and Germany respectively. The Marxist sees these as economic phenomena. To him they are due to the desperate machinations of Capitalists seeking to strengthen their last defensive positions. The multitude of Marxist works on the subject all revolve about this theme. Everything non-economic is dismissed as epiphenomenal, or as lies told by rogues to deceive dupes.

But to any unprejudiced person with even the slightest knowledge of the recent national movements of Italy and Germany, the Marxist interpretation is the grossest travesty. The doctrinaire Marxists with their economic pre-occupation have never understood the well-springs of these movements. They are like a man born deaf watching an audience listening to a musician, and, because he can hear no music, concluding that they must have some ulterior motive for their conduct.

Again, let us take as an example the Marxist view of religion.

On the Marxist theory the Church is merely an instrument for political suppression used by the exploiting class. Religion is the opiate of the people. The toleration accorded to religious observance in the Soviet Union today is reminiscent of the indulgence one might extend towards some fanciful belief of a child, in the expectation that in time he will grow out of it.

The Marxists have never really examined the grounds of religious belief and the purposes of religious institutions. Obedient to their general principles, they can see in religion and Churches merely an economic phenomenon, and they have never enquired deeper.

And yet, in these and all examples we might take, the Marxists themselves are satisfied with their own interpretation and point with pride to all the evidence they have to prove it. Without realising it, they are employing a Procrustean bed. They are selecting, lengthening out, or chopping off the facts until they all fit the pre-determined bed. The Marxists, having firmly made up their minds beforehand, and being ingenious people, can never be directly proved wrong about history. *They can always write history in their own way.*

The Procrustean device, once having been pointed out, is so obvious that we might ask—Why don't the Marxists realise it themselves? This is like the previous example of the logical positivists. Why don't the logical positivists realise the character of their starting point? Just as we could only suggest the psycho-therapist for the confirmed positivist, so it seems we must do likewise for the determined Marxist historian.

We cannot leave the subject without drawing attention to one significant feature of the theory of economic determinism. There are two forms to this theory: a strong and a weak. The weak version is that the economic background is a potent one in history. This is at least a possible view to hold. But the strong form of the theory: that the economic background *determines* the course of history, which is the typical Marxist form, is easily seen to be involved in a vicious circle. For if this is the case, then presumably the Marxist doctrine is itself historically determined by economic causes, both in its historical incidence and in its doctrinal content, in which case it is difficult to see what cogency the doctrine possesses. The only way out of the difficulty would be for the Marxist to claim for himself a special dispensation from the prevailing determinism. This ingenuous claim has in fact been made by some.[1] The great majority of Marxist writers, however, seem oblivious to the vicious circle in which they are caught.

This is comparable with all attempts to deny free will and uphold determinism. The upholding of a general determinism is self-refuting since to uphold it significantly the upholder must himself be exempted from it.

### The Class Struggle

Closely associated with the economic interpretation of history is the theory of the division of society into warring classes.

'The history of all hitherto existing society is the history of class struggles,' says the *Communist Manifesto*.[2] 'Freeman and slave, patrician and plebeian, lord and serf, guild master and journeyman, in a word oppressor and oppressed stood in constant opposition to one another, carried on an uninterrupted, now hidden, now open, fight, a fight that each time ended, either in a revolutionary reconstitution of society at large, or in the common ruin of the contending classes. . . .

'In our epoch, the epoch of the bourgeoisie, Society as a whole is more and more splitting up into two great hostile camps, into two great classes directly facing each other—bourgeoisie and proletariat.'

There is no doubt that pointing out the class stratification of our society, as distinct from some primitive societies, and

---

[1] As for instance :—' Only the proletariat, which has as its objective the creation of the classless society, is freed of limitations to its conception of the historical process and creates a true genuine history of nature and of society.' Hessen, B. : *The Social and Economic Roots of Newton's Principia*, Introduction.

[2] To this Engels adds the interesting note that primitive tribal society was communistic and classless. With the dissolution of primitive society a class-stratified society emerged. The future state of the world is of course envisaged as a return to a higher form of the classless society. We may represent this evolution by a dialectical triad :

$$\text{ONE} \searrow$$
$$\text{many}$$
$$\text{one} \nearrow$$

the tendency in our society to a class struggle, is a valuable contribution to the understanding of society and history.

But to turn the usually more or less vague and hierarchial and generally fairly pacific class divisions of society into a rigid categorial scheme of warring sections, is going far beyond anything that the facts warrant. The Marxists have erected a categorial system and have called it the real. Instead of being an enlightening contribution to history it has become a source of obscurantism. It has led to the view that the *normal* condition of our society is class struggle, instead of this being more like a *diseased* condition.

So far have the Marxists taken this supposed natural division, that they envisage a proletarian art as opposed to bourgeois art, and a proletarian morals as opposed to bourgeois morals. There is even a distinctive proletarian history.[1]

They see the future of the world lying with the proletariat. After the proletariat have overthrown the bourgeois, and after a period of proletarian dictatorship, the State will wither away and the world will enter into a new classless society.

But if we view history dispassionately we are more likely to arrive at the conclusion of Leo XIII that :

The great mistake that is made in the matter now under consideration is to possess oneself of the idea that class is naturally hostile to class ; that rich and poor are intended by nature to live at war with one another. So irrational and so false is this view that the exact contrary is the truth. . . . In a State it is ordained by nature that these two classes should exist in harmony and agreement, and should, as it were, fit into one another, so as to maintain the equilibrium of the body politic.[2]

There is no call here for any exhaustive discussion of the theory of a warring class structure. Enough has been said to show that it is an extreme theory. And yet no amount of argument or historical enquiry will shift the confirmed Marxist. He will insist that in every phase of our history, since the break up of primitive tribal society, he can find the class struggle at work as a vital force. The difference of opinion

[1] See p. 148, n. 1, quotation from Hessen.
[2] Encyclical : *Rerum Novarum* (1891).

with the Marxist is really not for him a factual one.  For he is running a Procrustean bed and he makes history fit into it. This means that he can never be forced to admit that he is wrong.  The theory of the class struggle is 'true' because the Marxist will never let it be untrue.  (c.f. the laws of Procrustean physics).  Why the Marxist runs this Procrustean bed is again a psychological matter.  He may have many unconscious motives.

An interesting sidelight on the class struggle principle is that its historical advocacy by the Marxists may be tending actually to bring it about.  For the Marxist theories have become widely known and have made many people 'class conscious' and hostile to the oppressing class.  This has no doubt developed and exacerbated whatever class struggle may have been there incipiently.  So the Marxists' Procrustean bed may be moulding not only past history, but the future as well, although in a manner different from that which the Marxists envisage on their own principles.  For the growing intensity of class warfare will not now be an economic phenomenon but an intellectual one.

Lenin once wrote[1] :

The proletariat is becoming enlightened and educated by waging its class struggle, it is ridding itself of the prejudices of bourgeois society ; it is rallying its ranks ever more closely, and is learning to gauge the measure of its successes, it is steeling its forces and is growing irresistibly.

Granting the fact, opinions may yet differ about its cause.

[1] Lenin : *Three Sources and Three Component Parts of Marxism.*

# CHAPTER XI

# SCIENTIFIC METHOD

*The Quest for a Scientific Method*

THE great success of physical science in the post-Renaissance world led to much speculation about the secret of its success. It has been the general opinion that this secret must lie in some way in the *method* employed in the new sciences. If we could discover precisely what this method is, and make it explicit, then, so it was thought, we should be able to use it more effectively, and, no doubt, extend its employment to even wider fields. Consequently ever since the 17th century much attention has been paid to the quest for this scientific method.

We have already considered Francis Bacon as the 'politician' of the new movement to extend man's power over Nature (Ch. IV). Francis Bacon was also the author of one of the first attempted formulations of the method of the new science. He laid down rules which he believed would, if followed, lead automatically to our complete mastery over Nature. His method consisted in collecting and recording all available facts, performing all practicable experiments, and finally, by means of certain rules, making out connections between all the phenomena so observed.

However, this procedure, or method, as laid down by Bacon, turns out on closer acquaintance to be barren. It is much too simple and naïve to meet the situation. Nature in fact is not nearly as simple and orderly as Bacon had supposed. The practising scientists went on developing their sciences along their own lines without reference to Bacon's supposed automatic method.

A modern author justly observes[1] :

The extreme difficulty and labour of finding laws of nature even when you know where and how to look, much more when it is a question of discovering a new one, suggest that there is not so much simplicity and order about as people think. If nature were really orderly through and through, it is probable that Bacon's notion would be correct, that given the correct procedure, any fool could discover laws ; but this is notoriously not the case. It is only as the result of the century-long labours of the wisest men that anything much has been discovered, and that as the result countless mistakes and false starts (*sic*). Even when we know what the laws of nature are, it is not such an easy business to observe their correctness in any instance, but it needs special training and special means to carry out the observations.

Although Bacon failed, the quest for the method of science has gone on, and a considerable literature has grown up on the subject.

The empiricist logicians of the John Stuart Mill school of thought worked along the lines of the 'Uniformity of Nature.' The simplest doctrine was that we observe uniformities in Nature and generalise them into laws. This theory of the method of science gained some plausibility from sciences like elementary astronomy, where the observation of uniformities and the generalisation into laws is indeed in some cases not far removed from the truth.

On the rôle of astronomy in this matter Ritchie makes the following comment :

It must be remembered that Astronomy was the first science to develop and the first to become exact, and this fact has coloured all subsequent thought. What plausibility the Principle of Uniformity has is due to the fact that among the heavenly bodies mere observation, without active interference in the course of events, reveals completely orderly behaviour.[2]

With the growth of the various sciences this simple doctrine became more and more inadequate to meet the situation, and more attention had to be paid to the rôle of the hypothesis.

[1] Ritchie, A. D. : *Scientific Method* (London, 1923), p. 201.
[2] *Ibid.* p. 93 n.

Mill himself makes passing reference to the subject of hypotheses in his *System of Logic*.

The consideration of hypotheses was, of course, a step in the direction of recognising that the scientist is not so much passive as active. But in the Mill era the notion of our activity was still very tentative. The hypothesis was then simply a slightly indirect means of *discovering* a uniformity. The idea that a uniformity could be *manufactured* was hardly contemplated.

With the continued growth of the sciences, and our gradually increasing insight into them, the spell of John Stuart Mill was eventually broken. An activity undreamt of by the generality of logicians in the 19th century is, in the 20th century, gaining more and more acceptance. *The activity contemplated today is not merely an activity in discovery, but an activity in manufacture, a formative activity, whereby we mould our subject matter.*

As yet logicians are hesitant and doubtful, and put forward such doctrines very cautiously. For instance Ritchie writes[1]:

I have argued that our general knowledge of the external world as expressed by laws of nature, is a product of the interaction of two processes, selection from and classification of what is experienced and the discovery of laws relating the classes. The two processes are linked together and in fact developed simultaneously, so that we adjust our classification in order to obtain general laws and apparently believe in our laws because of the excellence of our classification. It sounds as though there might be a vicious circle involved in this process.[2]

This then is approximately the point reached at the present day in the gradual evolution of general opinion about science and scientific method and scientific laws.

---

[1] *Ibid.* p. 79.

[2] It will be apparent that Ritchie is feeling his way towards the Procrustean theory of the ' natural ' laws expounded in this work. The author goes on to the assertion that apparently an act of faith is necessary at some point or other in the acceptance of the laws. But such a theological analogy is quite unjustified. We have shown in other chapters how pragmatism meets the situation, and that this is indeed the proper place for pragmatism.

### The Two Types of Science[1]

The extraordinary feature of the growth of opinion concerning the exact sciences, at least in English-speaking countries, is the almost universal neglect of the doctrines of Immanuel Kant. The name of Kant is scarcely mentioned in the standard works on scientific method today.

Contemporary logicians are slowly and painfully emancipating themselves from the thraldom of John Stuart Mill and the English Empiricists generally, and, apparently without realising it, are with great labour coming round to doctrines which were so brilliantly advanced by Kant a century and a half ago. This of course consists in the recognition of our formative activity in physical laws. (Ch. VI).

The only extenuating circumstance for this remarkable neglect is that Kant erected an elaborate philosophical structure on his theory of physics, and this structure has tended to block the view of the foundations to generations of later philosophers.

Kant pointed out that there are two sorts of science: *the receptive pupil* and *the stern judge* types,[2] i.e. the passive and the active. This is the most fundamental observation ever made about science in modern times. Its neglect has kept our understanding of the sciences centuries behind.

This distinction of Kant's makes the field of the modern sciences explicable. It is the key to the post-17th century panorama of sciences, and to neglect it leads to endless confusion.

The common accounts of scientific method are difficult, and even confused, because they make little or no distinction between the various sciences. They attempt to generalise from an amalgam containing members of fundamentally diverse natures. This being the case it is not to be wondered at that authors of works on scientific method find their subject difficult.

The exact science of physics belongs to the 'stern judge' class. A descriptive science like geology or botany, on the

---

[1] In this and following sections it is assumed that the reader is acquainted with the doctrines of earlier chapters. These doctrines are drawn on here summarily to show their bearing on the subject of ' scientific method.'

[2] *Kritik*, B xiii.

other hand, belongs predominantly to the 'receptive pupil' class. To find a common method in these two is a hopeless task. Every science should be considered on its own merits.

The term 'scientific method' is thus an unfortunate one, since the pursuit of a general method for all the sciences is illusory. Instead there is a method for each science, or perhaps better still there is a *practice* for each science. The flexibility of these practices is such that the term 'method' is hardly appropriate.

Considerations of scientific methods, or practices, come logically *after* the sciences, not before. There is no scientific method which, once possessed, will lead to the automatic development of the sciences.[1]

In fact there is no royal road to any science. Scientific training consists in a long and laborious apprenticeship to a *practice* which has been built up over centuries. These practices, while intricately methodical, are not 'methods' in any simple sense of the term. The practices are subtle, varied, and flexible. They take many years to acquire. Scientific training consists in getting the 'feel' of things, rather than being inculcated into a cut and dried method. This may seem inexplicable to the non-scientist, but all who have actually worked at scientific pursuits in the laboratory will doubtless agree on the truth of this contention.[2]

## Pairs of Sciences

The 'stern judge' sciences are the Procrustean categorial sciences like modern physics. The real or natural sciences belong to the 'receptive pupil' class, as for instance botany and zoology.

---

[1] In popular thought, ' scientific method ' has sometimes been regarded as a sort of Aladdin's lamp which, when rubbed, would summon the scientific genie to our bidding. This notion is of course quite without foundation.

[2] It is sometimes held that a training in ' scientific method ' will make better scientists. This is very doubtful. If scientific method comes not before, but after, scientific practice, then it can hardly assist in the practice. In fact anything which tends to endanger the flexibility of scientific practices is rather to be discouraged.

Similarly a study of ' aesthetics ' is full of dangers for the artist, although it may be a great help in our *understanding* of art.

A given subject matter can be cultivated either as it really is, in which case we have a real science; or it can be subjected to a categorial treatment, in which case we have a categorial science. In principle there should be this duality in every branch of science. Each branch should consist of a pair of members, one 'real,' the other 'categorial' or 'Procrustean.'

Aristotle and St. Thomas cultivated, to the best of their abilities, the real member of each branch. The Procrustean members of the pairs properly got under way only in the 17th century. Physics was the first to be launched, and is still far ahead of all the others. In biology on the other hand we are today still attending almost entirely to the real member, with perhaps a slight admixture of the Procrustean creeping in. But on the whole the Procrustean member in biology seems to have scarcely yet started. Other sciences are in various stages of transition.[1]

The notion that there is a method in the sciences probably arises in part from the contemplation of the real members of the doublets. These real members are, in principle, continuous with metaphysics, and metaphysics should provide us with a method for developing them. This was indeed the case when the Aristoteleans cultivated the sciences, for they cultivated the real sciences.

But the continuity with metaphysics is *not* the case with the Procrustean member of each doublet. This member is autonomous, and metaphysics cannot supply a method here. In fact there is nothing we can properly call a scientific method for the Procrustean sciences.

---

[1] Owing to the confusion on the matter, it has not hitherto been the practice to cultivate *both* members of a doublet simultaneously. It has been thought erroneously that they are antagonistic, whereas they are properly complementary and should co-exist in harmony. Thus the new physics of Galileo and his contemporaries ousted the real physics of the ancient and medieval period. The latter has made no progress since the close of the Middle Ages. Let us hope that now the situation has become clearer the pursuit of a neo-Aristotelean physics will be resumed parallel to the pursuit of Galilean physics.

It is interesting to notice that in this respect the medieval philosophers were wiser than the modern (see Appendix).

*Discovery and Demonstration*

We have doubted the appropriateness of the notion of a general method for the Procrustean sciences. But at least this element of method may be recognised : that there is DISCOVERY, and there is DEMONSTRATION, and these are two quite different processes.

Demonstration is the empirical testing to ascertain to what extent a proposed theory is a success. The process is, in principle, relatively simple and uniform.

Discovery on the other hand is varied and complex, and indeed often fortuitous. An idea or hypothesis which subsequently proves fruitful may come from almost any source. *It is not the source of the hypothesis which guarantees it, but the subsequent empirical demonstration of its success.* Particularly in the early days of modern physics, prior metaphysical considerations were often drawn upon to furnish ideas for testing. It is surprising how often even today metaphysical beliefs will furnish suggestions to the physicist. But metaphysical validity or invalidity has no bearing on value as a scientific hypothesis.

Another fruitful source is analogy. Analogy in itself establishes nothing, but it has often given fruitful ideas, and in fact it is probably the greatest source of new ideas open to the physicist.[1]

There are various other sources of theories which might be suggested, but we have mentioned enough to illustrate the present theme of the dichotomy between discovery and demonstration.

The distinction between discovery and demonstration or verification is characteristic of the autonomous Procrustean sciences. It is *not* the case with the real members of the doublets. With the real members the dichotomy between discovery and verification no longer holds.

*Philosophy's Grey in Grey*

We have already pointed out how large a part astronomy has played in the past in forming the ideas of the classical

[1] See e.g. de Solages : *Dialogue sur L'Analogie*, Ch. II. for an interesting account of the rôle of analogy in physical science.

empiricist writers on scientific method. Astronomy is peculiar in that it is one science where experiment is virtually ruled out. Consequently its Procrustean character is comparatively undeveloped.[1] Yet this semi-realist science was widely used as a model and prototype to formulate a method for use in the general field of physics, although the latter was becoming ever more Procrusteanised.

The classical empiricist logicians, in their theories of scientific method, were in fact harking back to a state of affairs which had generally prevailed several centuries previously, but which was becoming increasingly outmoded and inapt in their own times.

In this lagging behind, the logicians are following a parallel course to the political philosophers. The favourite theme of writers on political theory in the 17th and 18th centuries was the social contract. Yet in reality the social contract had little or no meaning as applied to the sovereign states of their day. The period when the social contract did have some meaning was several centuries earlier, in the feudal period, when there was some sort of contract between lord and serfs.

But for some time now the political philosophers have advanced to the point of recognising the place of sovereignty as the essence of the state. Unfortunately for the philosophers, however, there are not lacking some who maintain that they are still hopelessly in the rear. For, so it is contended, the essence of the modern state is no longer sovereignty but public service.[2]

We might, too, cast a glance back as far as Aristotle, and draw attention to Aristotle's continuing adherence to the theory of the city-state when the world under Alexander was rapidly being transformed into sovereign empires.

Hegel summed up the whole situation in his famous dictum : When philosophy paints its grey in grey, then has a shape of life

---

[1] See however the Appendix, where we trace the development of ancient and medieval astronomical theories. The character of these theories is more complex than might be supposed at first sight.

[2] See Duguit, Leon : *Law in the Modern State* (London, 1921).

grown old. By philosophy's grey in grey it cannot be rejuvenated but only understood. The owl of Minerva spreads its wings only with the falling of the dusk.[1]

While most of the philosophers of modern science were centuries behind the times, yet there were a few who saw more clearly. Such a one was Immanuel Kant. But his was a voice crying in the wilderness. It is only today that Kant is coming into his own.

[1] Hegel : *Philosophy of Right* (tr. Knox), (Oxford, 1942), Preface, p. 13.

# CHAPTER XII

# NON-EUCLIDEAN GEOMETRIES

*The Two Orders in Mathematics*

AN interesting development in mathematics in modern times is the introduction of geometries alien to the geometry of Euclid. Two noted non-Euclidean geometries are those of Riemann and Lobatchewsky. Among Euclid's postulates is the 'parallel postulate,' which states that through a given point outside a given straight line, one, and only one, coplanar straight line can be drawn parallel to the given straight line. In Lobatchewskyan geometry, however, a *sheaf* of lines can be drawn through the given point so as not to cut the given straight line. In Riemannian geometry *no* line can be drawn through the point parallel to the given straight line.

Remarkable as these non-Euclidean postulates may seem to be, yet they lead to systems of geometry which are internally self-consistent.

In general we can generate a non-Euclidean geometry by varying *any* of Euclid's postulates, as we please. Consequently a great number of non-Euclidean geometries are possible in principle.

In accordance with the general doctrine of this work we may put Euclid's geometry into the real order and liken it to the real physics which was being cultivated before the days of Galileo, and to the real logic which is the subject of the classical logicians.

Just as modern systems of 'physics' are of Procrustean artifacts withdrawn from the real corporeal world, and modern 'logics' are of categorial artifacts removed from the conceptual representation of the real world of being, so non-Euclidean geometries are systems of artifacts removed from the conceptual representation of the real world of space.

Accordingly when a mathematical physicist says, for instance, that the universe is finite with such and such a radius, he is telling us nothing of the real order (though if he is confused he may believe that he is). What he is telling us in truth is that he is employing a Riemann geometry in his cosmology, and that it gives such and such results. This is the only significance of his pronouncement; he is perfectly entitled to carry on this activity if he pleases. But he his giving us no information concerning the real nature of the universe and its geometry.

We have suggested that there is one real geometry and a multitude of artifact geometries. Similarly in regard to other movements in mathematics. There have been developed in recent times systems, for instance, of non-commutative algebra. We might regard these systems as analogous to non-Euclidean geometries, and as having a similar artifact character.

Again, many-dimensional spaces are frequently employed in modern mathematics and mathematical physics. In general we may employ a space of $n$-dimensions, where $n$ is any number we please, instead of being restricted to the properties of the space where $n = 3$.

But here again we regard the space where $n = 3$ as the real, and the space where $n > 3$ as belonging to the order of artifacts.

And, as a last instance, what is the status of 'unreal' or 'complex' numbers in mathematics? It seems likely that the whole realm of 'unreal' numbers is a system of artifacts.

Right through mathematics there runs this same division. There is a mathematics of the real order; and there is a multiplicity of mathematics of an artifact order.

Kronecker expressed this division when he said 'God made the natural numbers, man made the rest.' Kronecker may or may not have drawn the dividing line at the right point. This is a matter to be decided by detailed examination and reflection. But the idea of a dichotomy of this nature is quite sound.

*Mathematical Relativism*

Some mathematical writers explain this division into two orders in a different manner. Their contention is that the division is not so much real as psychological. They say, e.g. that we regard Euclidean geometry as the real geometry, and the others as unreal, because the Euclidean principles have been ingrained into us by long custom. In reality, they maintain, *all* geometries, Euclidean included, are on the same footing. There is, so to speak, no *absolute* geometry.

This contention, which is popular among mathematical philosophers today,[1] is closely allied to the more general contention that there is no absolute knowledge at all. This thesis of general scepticism is discussed in detail in works on Epistemology. It is readily seen to be self-contradictory and untenable. There is no need to discuss the topic here beyond pointing out that the mere enunciation of such a doctrine is itself an 'absolute,' and consequently the doctrine is self-refuting. *Universal scepticism or relativism cannot be propounded without denying itself.*

That the Euclidean geometry is in fact an 'absolute' geometry, and is not merely held to be so by ingrained convention, is something which should not be difficult to prove apodeictically. Similar considerations apply with other systems of mathematical artifacts, like the non-commutative algebras, the multi-dimensional spaces, the unreal numbers, and so on, which we have already mentioned.

It is significant that we cannot really '*think*' in terms of a non-Euclidean geometry, or a multi-dimensional space, etc. We can indeed employ the rules and manipulate the mathematical symbols in which these systems are formulated, so that we can '*work*' with these systems, *but we are all the time thinking, when we do think, in terms of the Euclidean geometry and the 3-dimensional space.* 'Thinking' on the one hand, and 'working' according to rules on the other, are two quite different processes.

The very formulation of the non-Euclidean schemes takes

[1] e.g. Poincaré (see p. 105).

place from a background of Euclidean geometry. The Euclidean geometry is always implicitly pre-supposed. It is assumed in the very act of its denial, and consequently it cannot be meaningfully denied. Similarly with the other non-classical mathematical systems.

Those who hold that this inability to think and reason discursively except in 3-dimensional Euclidean space, etc., is merely a psychological habit, have never advanced any evidence for their belief. They have put forward this psychological theory merely to enable them to uphold a relativistic doctrine of knowledge.

A similar discussion proceeds in the logical field as regards the status of the classical logic. The modern logicians, or some of them, claim that we tend to accept the classical logic as being 'absolute' because of ingrained habit or some such cause. In reality, it is held, all logics are on the same footing. This again is parallel to the contention of general scepticism in knowledge, and can be dealt with similarly. Relativism in logic is inherently self-refuting.[1]

These artifact systems are developed by the pure mathematician as an intellectual exercise. They are employed by the applied mathematician and the mathematical physicist because they are often useful tools for the work to be done : tools to be taken up or dropped at will. In developing, say, the kinetic theory of gases it may be convenient to work in terms of an *n*-dimensional space. *But the introduction of the symbols for such a space, and their subsequent manipulation, gives no absolute status whatever to n-dimensional spaces.* It is from first to last a device, a fiction, an artifact, as we have called such things, whereby we facilitate the work in hand.

Again, in the mathematical theory of alternating currents, and indeed in the theory of vibrations in general, the employment of complex numbers, while not essential, nevertheless gives rise to a very elegant treatment. But complex numbers are not thereby rendered 'absolute.' Their status is that of a tool.

[1] See Chs. VIII and XVI.

So much for the motives for developing these systems. Now here again is the important point : *when the matter is, on the contrary, one of pure reason, as distinct from mathematical manipulation, we cannot escape from the classical mathematics of Euclid, etc.*

### Kant's Theory of Mathematics

We have already seen how Kant in *The Critique of Pure Reason* suggested that an *a priori* revolution had occurred in mathematics similar to that in physics (p. 76 f.). Kant himself thought that the *a priori* approach had been introduced at the commencement of Euclidean geometry. In this he was mistaken however. We can see now that the revolution in mathematics applies not to classical mathematics, but to the artifact systems of pure mathematics found in non-Euclidean geometries, multi-dimensional spaces, etc.

Kant was in error here as an historian, but he was curiously correct in anticipation of the character of the modern systems.

# CHAPTER XIII

# SOCIETY AND MORALS

## *Law and Morality*

LANGUAGE is one of the great instruments of human society. The legislative activity of society in the realm of language, and the logic of language which results from it, we have already considered.

Law, in the legal sense of the body of law, is another of the great instruments of society. Indeed, the law which it has produced, like the language, is one of the most fundamental facts about any given society.

With language we have the duality of words and things ; so with law we have the duality of law and morals. In each case the first member of the pair belongs to the social order, the categorial order, the realm of *nomos*. The second member belongs to the real order, the realm of *physis*. In each case society has created a structure which runs in double harness with the structure of the real or natural world.

Morality is properly real and objective. But the law in an actual state sits loosely on morality.[1]

The law is permeated by the categorial. In so far as moral issues are involved there is a practical difficulty in rising always to the moral level in courts of law, and embarking on the subtleties of detailed casuistry. This necessitates a more arbitrary categorial scheme for administration, imperfect though such a scheme may be. Hence the necessity for the legislature and the body of the law. Hence too the necessity for 'equity' to moderate the cleavage between the categorial and the real.

---

[1] In the ideal state, as envisaged by St. Thomas Aquinas, the human positive law would be everywhere in perfect conformity with the natural law. But in actual states there is usually something less than this perfect harmony of positive law and natural law (see Ch. II).

The civil law in modern states frequently departs widely from the natural law, i.e. from morality, in matters such as e.g. adultery, divorce, tolerance, education, and so on.

As an example of how far the legal order may inadvertently depart from the real order, here in a matter not specifically moral, we might mention the English law on mental deficiency as it formerly stood. The Mental Deficiency Act of 1913 defined the classes of idiots, imbeciles, feeble-minded, and moral imbeciles. But further investigation rendered it very doubtful if there is any such thing as ' moral imbecility,' i.e. moral imbecility not associated with mental defect also.[1] As a consequence of this :

the legal classification of moral imbecility soon became in reality a convenient administrative method of providing for mental defectives who were in addition persistent delinquents, or for delinquents who urgently needed some effective control, yet who were not so obviously mentally deficient in the ordinary sense of the word as to conform to the definition of mental defect within the meaning of the Act.[2]

In this case the legislative category, intended to refer to the real, turned out to be in all probability quite artificial, but nevertheless still of some use in practical administration.

The general situation is not, as is sometimes alleged, that law and morality pertain to different fields. They pertain for the most part to the same field, but they deal with it in different ways. *Morality attends to the real order, to the situation as it objectively is. Law attends to that situation after it has been subjected to a categorial transformation, i.e. after the legal categories have been impressed upon it.*

Law is a blunt instrument by practical necessity. It is as blunt as its categories. Morality on the other hand, is, in principle, infinitely refined. It knows no limit to its probing, nor to its sensitivity.

A modern author on Jurisprudence writes thus :

While the sphere of ethics may remain the same, that of law will widen or narrow according to the particular social philosophy

---

[1] See Cammack, J. S. : *Moral Problems of Mental Defect* (London, 1939).
[2] *Ibid.* p. 132.

adopted by the community. What are today regarded as purely religious duties were once enforced by law ; conversely modern law will enforce many rules designed to save the individual from himself in a way that would have seemed absurd to a disciple of *laissez-faire*. There is no immutable boundary to the area of operation of law.[1]

This is a fair statement of law as it is in the modern state. Law in the modern state follows closely the Austinian definition, that law is fundamentally the *Will* of the Sovereign. This is in direct contrast with the medieval theory that law is fundamentally *Reason* and so is in conformity with, and subject to, the dictates of natural morality.[2]

In our terminology, the medieval ideal was to have law in the closest possible association with the real order, which is the subject of reason. In modern times the tendency has been for law to move further and further away from the real order into a more or less autonomous categorial order of its own, subject not primarily to reason but to will.

This transition to a categorial order is not necessarily vicious. But it has to be very carefully controlled in order that it may not become so.

We might observe here that the Nazi conception of jurisprudence was designed to bridge more effectively the gulf between law and morals. (Though here the morals may or may not have been the same as the traditional).

Law, traditionally, is relatively fixed, constant and precise. It gains these qualities, as we have seen, by a drastic limitation of its range and depth. The German jurists have moved in the opposite direction, they have expanded the notion of law and brought it into contact with every aspect of life. They have made it dynamic, flexible, and fluid. The law for them is no longer static and categorial. It is the spirit which counts in this system, and the judge must be one whose essence is in communion with the Führer and the race.[3]

---

[1] Paton, G. : *A Text Book of Jurisprudence* (Oxford, 1946), p. 58.

[2] See *Christian Philosophy in the Common Law*, by Richard O'Sullivan (Oxford, 1947), for an interesting discussion from this point of view of the evolution of the English Common Law.

[3] See Barker, Sir Ernest : *Reflections on Government* (Oxford, 1942), pp. 394 ff.

It is plain then that the main tendency of Nazi jurisprudence was to shift law from the categorial order across into the real order, or what was considered to be the real order. The freedom of English case law tends in the same direction, but to a much lesser extent.

## Ethics and Social Science

Since the 17th century physical science has gone ahead in its autonomous career at an ever-accelerating pace. In more recent times many attempts have been made to found a science of human affairs, a science which, it is hoped, will have a career as brilliant as its physical counterpart.

It seems likely that in the emergence of this new social science, if indeed it does positively emerge, the story of the birth of 17th century physical science will be re-enacted. On one side will be the rational ethics of the *philosophia perennis*. On the other the new empirical science of human affairs. They will be *prima facie* in conflict, just as in the 17th century the Aristotelean learning was *prima facie* in conflict with the new empirical learning.

That such a conflict is even now in progress is an opinion widely held today. This growing *prima facie* conflict has been the subject of a recent study by the President of the Superior Institute of Philosophy at Louvain, the Rt. Rev. Simon Deploige.[1] The study is directed particularly to the work of the French sociologists, Durkheim and Lévy-Bruhl, but many of its observations are appropriate to a wider horizon.

Just as in the 17th century most of the proponents of the new sciences believed that there was an irreconcilable opposition between themselves and the Aristoteleans, so the latter day social scientists believe that there is a fundamental conflict between the new sociology and the old ethics. 'We must make a choice between the two,' says Lévy-Bruhl.[2]

The supposed conflict is summed up by Deploige thus :

Ethics OR sociology ; we are told to choose between them.

---

[1] Deploige, S. : *The Conflict between Ethics and Sociology* (Eng. tr. St. Louis, Mo., 1938).

[2] Quoted by Deploige, *ibid.* p. 1.

Ethics is said to be the past with its ignorance, naïve or affected, or its pretensions, chimerical or harmful. Its insufficiency is no longer a secret, and the criticism of the sociologists completes the exposure of its decline.[1]

What sociology does, according to its proponents, is to :

undertake the positive study of moral facts of the present and of the past. And in place of the ancient academic speculation about concepts, it will substitute the scientific investigation of the laws of reality. Finally, later on, the theoretical knowledge will be applied. A rational art, moral or social, will be founded, which will profit by the discoveries of science. It will employ the knowledge of sociological laws in the improvement of morals and of existing institutions.[2]

*However, after a careful study of this new sociology, Deploige arrives at the conclusion that in truth there is not, and indeed cannot be, a conflict between ethics and sociology.* The common opinion, on the part of the sociologists, that there is such a conflict, is due to a misunderstanding of the situation (cf. the mistaken opposition of the 17th century exponents of the new physical sciences to the Aristotelean metaphysical principles).

Deploige sees in the new social sciences a prolongation of the Thomistic conception of moral and political science, and he concludes :

The history of religions, the comparative science of laws and institutions, social economy, demography, ethnography, statistics—or, if you prefer, sociology in its diverse departments—work to enrich moral and social philosophy with new data and useful information. They bring to the place of construction materials which will permit the repair of the edifice and the continuance of its development. Between them and Thomistic moral philosophy there should exist a useful collaboration. Only ignorance can pretend that there is a conflict between them.[3]

The parallel between the growth of the social sciences today and of the physical sciences three centuries ago, leads us to expect that as the social sciences develop, they will, like the physical sciences, become more and more Procrustean and

[1] *Ibid.* p. 355.
[2] *Ibid.* pp. 13–14.
[3] *Ibid.* p. 380.

categorial.[1]  We may expect them to employ laws and concepts more and more alien to the real ethics.  But this growing disparity between the two will not mean a conflict.  For they belong to different orders, and consequently cannot in themselves conflict.  The social science in its categorial order is rightly autonomous, but it must always be recognised that it *is* of the categorial order, and not the real order.

It yet remains to be seen, of course, whether and to what extent an actual science of human affairs can be made practically successful as an instrument of social engineering.  So far the results do not seem to be very encouraging, but the science is still young, and the first steps are the hardest.

One factor in the success of a categorial science is necessarily the tractability of the material.  It may well be that the material of the social sciences is inherently much more intractable than that of the physical sciences.  Considering the free will of man this seems highly likely.  If this be the case it explains why the social sciences lag so far behind the physical sciences in spite of all efforts to push on the former.

[1] cf. Ch. XIV on ' *History as a Science.* '

# CHAPTER XIV

# HISTORY AS A SCIENCE

*Professor Collingwood*

THE modern progressive science of physics commenced when, in the words of Kant, we ceased to be like the pupil listening to everything the teacher chooses to say, but instead, like a judge, compelled Nature to answer questions which we ourselves had formulated. It has been suggested in recent years that a progressive science of history might be started if a like Copernican revolution could be brought about in historical studies.

The late Professor R. G. Collingwood was one of the leading exponents of this view.[1] His thought is permeated through and through with Kant's great idea about the Galilean epistemology, and he believed he could see a future for history as brilliant as the career of physics since Galileo.

He writes in his *Autobiography*[2] :—

Until the late 19th and early 20th centuries, historical studies had been in a condition analogous to that of natural science before Galileo. In Galileo's time something happened to natural science (only a very ignorant or a very learned man would undertake to say briefly what it was) which suddenly and enormously increased the velocity of its progress and the width of its outlook. About the end of the 19th century something of the same kind was happening, more gradually and less spectacularly perhaps, but not less certainly, to history.

. . . It seemed to me as nearly certain as anything in the future could be, that historical thought, whose constantly increasing importance had been one of the most striking features of the 19th

---

[1] We have already discussed Collingwood's neo-Kantian theory of metaphysics in Ch. VII.

[2] Collingwood : *Autobiography*, Ch. VIII.

century, would increase in importance far more rapidly during the 20th ; and that we might very well be standing on the threshold of an age in which history would be as important for the world as natural science had been between 1600 and 1900.

History in the past was what Collingwood calls a ' scissors and paste affair.' This was like physics before Galileo. Collingwood writes :

If historians could only repeat, with different arrangements and different styles of decoration, what others had said before them, the age-old hope of using it as a school of political wisdom was as vain as Hegel knew it to be when he made his famous remark that the only thing to be learnt from history is that nobody ever learns anything from history.

But what if history is not a scissors and paste affair ? *What if the historian resembles the natural scientist in asking his own questions, and insisting on an answer ?* Clearly, that altered the situation.[1]

The past with which the historian deals is not a dead past, but a past which is living on in the present. With the Copernican revolution in our approach to this living past, history, so Collingwood hopes, will become a school of moral and political wisdom.

Collingwood speaks of political ' wisdom' being the Baconian fruits of this revolution. But on the analogy of the natural sciences 'wisdom' seems hardly the right term. Terms such as power, control, utility, prediction, would be more appropriate. This really is what Collingwood envisages in other passages, He writes[2] :

It was a plain fact that the gigantic increase since about 1600 in his power to control Nature had not been accompanied by a corresponding increase, or anything like it, in his power to control human situations. . . .

It was the widening of the scientific outlook and the acceleration of scientific progress in the days of Galileo that had led in the fullness of time from the water-wheels and windmills of the Middle Ages to the almost incredible power and delicacy of the modern machine. In dealing with their fellow men, I could see, men were still what they were in dealing with machines in the Middle Ages.

[1] *Ibid.* Ch. IX.
[2] *Ibid.* Ch. IX.

Well meaning babblers talked about the necessity for a change of heart. But the trouble was obviously in the head. What was needed was not more good will and human affection, but more understanding of human affairs and *more knowledge of how to handle them.*

This increase in our ability to handle human affairs, then, is to be brought about by the same revolution which transformed natural science in the 17th century, the nature of which revolution was first recognised by Immanuel Kant.

As Collingwood sees it, history as a science of human affairs did not begin to emerge until the 20th century. In the pre-scientific history age men perforce searched elsewhere for a science of human affairs. The 18th century looked for a ' science of human nature.' The 19th century sought for it in the shape of psychology. These both turned out to be illusory. But since the revolution in history, history has revealed itself as the one true science of human affairs.[1]

## The Two Histories

We might point out, however, something which Collingwood does not make clear, and about which he was probably not at all clear himself. This is the matter to which we drew attention when we doubted the appropriateness of the word ' wisdom ' for the knowledge acquired through the new science of history, and suggested such epithets as control, power, utility, etc., in its place. For, as we have insisted throughout this book, the fact that we have a Procrustean science does not mean that we have in any way abolished the structure of Nature, or that we can no longer know Nature in the way in which the *philosophia perennis* knows it.

Collingwood's proposed Kantian revolution in history will give us, of course, a Procrustean categorial science of history. *But real objective history will carry on just as before.* The relation between the two will be like the relation of modern so-called 'physics' to real physics, i.e. of *nomos* to *physis.*[2] The term

---

[1] *Ibid.* Ch. X.
[2] cf. e.g. modern sociology on the one hand and ethics on the other (Ch. XIII), or Freudian therapeutic psychology and rational psychology (Ch. XV).

'wisdom' is more appropriate to knowledge of the *physis* than to the categorial structure devised by the ingenuity of man. The latter, in the case of history, is a practical instrument of manipulation for the prince, the former is the pursuit of the real nature of history.

## The Character of Scientific History

Collingwood laid down the general principle which must be followed if history is to become a science, but he did not pursue the subject into specific terms.

We might develop a scheme of procedure in history by following the analogy of modern physics. This suggests the introduction into history of laws, fictions, artificial constructions, etc., as in physics. The concepts of ordinary life must be replaced by others more convenient for our purpose. For instance, in the exact physical sciences, the English term 'hard,' which is a familiar and vague expression, is replaced by a number of artificial but exact terms, such as malleability, shear modulus, tensile strength, etc. This would lead to a monstrous jargon in history akin to the formidable technical terminology of the Procrustean natural sciences. The new Procrustean history would now be only for specialists and would soon become as unintelligible to the layman as is modern physics. But its justification, if indeed it could be constructed, would be the pragmatic sanction of practical utility. It would be a handy machine for princes. It should be remembered too that the new history would be potentially a dangerous weapon, just as dangerous, if not more so, than the control we now possess over inanimate Nature.[1]

Whether such a Procrustean scheme will ever be born remains to be seen. For the inherent tractability or intractability of the raw material forming the primary subject matter of the Procrustean science must have some bearing on the ease with which such a science can be developed. The Procrustean method has had its greatest triumph in modern

[1] See pp. 58-9.

physics. In the biological sciences it has made much less progress, and in the human sciences and history has hardly started. Is this comparative failure outside physics due merely to dilatoriness and ineptitude, or is there a more underlying cause : that the subject matter in the animate and rational worlds is so much more intractable that it does not lend itself to Procrusteanisation ?

If a Procrustean history does emerge, as Collingwood hopes, there may possibly be in consequence an initial reaction away from classical history, like the reaction away from Aristotelean science, and indeed all things Aristotelean, in the times of Galileo. But such a reaction in historical studies would be as ill-founded as was the 17th century reaction.

Let wiser counsels prevail, and the two pursuits may go on side by side. To prevent confusion of the two, which caused so much trouble with the old and new physical sciences, it would be better to find a new name for the new Procrustean history. To go on calling it 'history' would be a perpetual source of confusion with real history. We would suggest the term *nomics* except that we have already applied that term to post-Galilean 'physics.' No doubt some new term appropriate to the situation could be found.

# CHAPTER XV

## SYSTEMS OF PSYCHOLOGY

WE have already discussed a number of sciences, physics logic, law, etc., in terms of a parallelism, with one component in each science belonging to the real order, and a number of components belonging to the categorial order. We will now turn our attention to the science of psychology where we will suggest a similar dualism. In particular we will examine the nature of what may be broadly termed Freudian psychology.

It has commonly been supposed that the Freudians are concerned to unravel the nature and functioning of the human mind : that the whole fascinating story which they have to tell about the subconscious, the ego, the id, sublimations, repressions, complexes, projections, etc., is a true and literal account of the mind and its workings.

But is this ' realist ' interpretation of Freud justified, or is the nature of Freudian psychology more like the Procrustean nature of modern physics which we upheld in Ch. III ? To what extent are the various Freudian concepts real, and to what extent are they categorial and Procrustean ? To the extent to which they are Procrustean we can see that they have been invented and applied so as to work in practice. And there is no doubt that Freudian psychology stands or falls on its practical fruits in the hands of the psychiatrist in correcting mental abnormalities. If it had no practical success in this field it would probably be dismissed, for the most part at least, as the fanciful product of a highly imaginative and romantic mind : namely that of Sigmund Freud.[1]

[1] We might notice another practical application of the Freudian psychology. In the hands of some, at least, of its exponents it tends to become a system of intimidation to quell their enemies. This no doubt is a misuse of the system, but it accounts for some of its popularity.

There is a fundamental weakness in the system, when regarded as of the real order, analogous to that of logical positivism and the theory of economic determinism. The weakness is that by its own criterion its originators and propagators are liable to its own diagnoses. In other words Freud's own peculiarities (he would have been a remarkable man indeed if he had had none) must have influenced his formulation. Consequently the system of psycho-analysis is caught up in a vicious circle. The psycho-analysts seem to assume implicitly that they are in some way exempt from their own processes. In this they are like the enthusiastic exponent of determinism who implicitly assumes that he is out of the grip of determinism. Otherwise, of course, as we have pointed out before, his formulation of determinism would itself be determined, so it is difficult to see what significance it would have, seeing that the formulator can't help saying what he does. Denial of free will is self-refuting.

It is self-refutation of this kind which runs through so much modern philosophy and to which we have drawn attention again and again.

The verdict on Freud of a contemporary philosopher of downright opinions and independent mind might be worth quoting here :—

. . . But when I came to study Freud's works I was not unprepared for the discovery that they reached a very high scientific level when dealing with problems in psychotherapy, but sank beneath contempt when they treated of ethics, politics, religion, or social structure. Nor was it strange that Freud's imitators and rivals, less intelligent and less conscientious writers whom I will not name, reached on these subjects an even lower level.[1]

This re-affirms our contention that Freudian psychology stands or falls on its practical fruits in therapy.

The extent to which the psycho-analysts can point to practical fruitfulness is the extent to which we can take the theory seriously. *But taking it seriously does not mean taking it as 'real,' for, as the case of modern physics so clearly showed, a*

[1] Collingwood, R. G. : *Autobiography*, Ch. IX.

*Procrustean scheme may be very successful and yet have no direct relation to the real state of affairs at all.*

In other words *the Freudian system may be merely a manipulative technique elaborated with an eye to mental therapy, and nothing more. It may give us no information about the real nature of mind.*

To the extent to which this is true the system escapes from the vicious circle in which it is otherwise caught. But it also follows that it is now useless going to the psycho-analyst and asking him questions about the real order, e.g. whether the will is free or determined, whether there is moral responsibility for acts, or whether all crime is a disease, whether religion is a neurosis, and so on. If the psycho-analyst can indeed give any answers to these questions the answers will be in the categorial order, and will not be genuine answers to questions directed to the real order.

In fact, to the extent to which Freudian psychology is Procrustean, the situation is not unlike that with Kant, who envisaged two selves, the phenomenal and the noumenal. The phenomenal self is that known in terms of the categories and is determined. But the noumenal self, which is unknown because of the inescapable categories, is free.

On this new Freudian categorial scheme the categories are now not rigid and unalterable, but flexible and pragmatic. Further, they being not inescapable, we *can* know the real 'noumenal' self simply by examining the self without imposing the Freudian categories. In the Freudian categorial order the will may be fixed, whereas in the real order we may know it to be free.

*Hence we can have the Freudian psychology side by side with the psychology of the real order, and without a clash.* But it must always be remembered that the Freudian system is only for practical use. The elements of the system must not be hypostatised.

This of course is parallel to the distinction we drew between modern Procrustean ' physics ' (*nomos*) and the ancient pursuit of the real physics (*physis*).

Precisely to what extent Freudian psychology is in fact

categorial, and to what extent it tells us about the real order, is something which could only be decided by careful and detailed consideration. *Prima facie* at least it would seem that the greater part of it is of the Procrustean character.[1]

Here again we have a case where a Procrustean bed, recognised as such, is valuable and beneficial, while unrecognised it leads to confusion and obscurantism.

Finally let us make it clear that these considerations are not put forward to deprecate the Freudian psychology. On the contrary, they are put forward in order that we might arrive at a clearer understanding of that psychology.

---

[1] There is a general analogy between Freud's system of psychology and Plato's doctrine of the nature of the soul. What Plato expresses in general and even metaphorical terms, Freud lays down as a specific system. The broad structure made out by Plato is hardened by Freud into a rigid scheme. Perhaps it is for the most part in this increased rigidity that we may look for the Freudian transition from the real to the categorial order.

# CHAPTER XVI

# ARTIFACTS

*God does not make rational beings ; it is a mark of the weakness of our abstract intelligence that in so many cases it has no power to conform itself to reality except by constructing these rational beings.*

JACQUES MARITAIN

## Mental Artifacts

WE have discussed in detail in previous chapters the relation between *physis* and *nomos*, or the real and the categorial, in a variety of different activities.

Here we will draw the threads together and examine more closely the way in which the doctrine of the two orders harmonises with the Scholastic logic, and how it is related to the theory of universals in Scholastic philosophy.

The doctrines propounded in this work constitute a study of what we might call *artifacts*. They are not indeed artifacts made by the hands of man. Instead they are artifacts constituted by our mental and social activities. In this sense the laws of Procrustean physics are artifacts. The categorial entities of the legal order are artifacts. The conventional usage of language gives birth to an elaborate system of artifacts. And so on.

The world of artifacts is an *autonomous* world. It has its own relations, connections, laws.

The artifact world is of a different order from the real world. The real world has been explored by the classical logicians and metaphysicians of the *philosophia perennis*. But it is only in recent times with Immanuel Kant, and latterly such philosophers as John Wisdom, that the exploration of the world of artifacts has been seriously undertaken. Even now the exploration is rather a reconnaissance than a full survey.

A great hindrance to work in both fields has been the common confusion between the two orders. This has led explorers of the artifact world to misunderstand the classical logicians and metaphysicians, and to earn for themselves the name of anti-metaphysicians. It has led the proponents of the *philosophia perennis* to underrate the new schools of philosophy. The confusion is accentuated by the similarity of nomenclature in the two orders, in both the physical and the social realms.

Where there is a state of confusion there is a standing challenge to dispel it. This is our objective here.

### Logic and Universals

Let us make it quite clear what the position is. We are *not* propounding a philosophical nominalism or conceptualism in opposition to the Scholastic moderate realism. The Scholastic doctrine is accepted here in its entirety.

The *nominalist* believes that there exists nothing but singular concrete objects. We select a group of concrete objects which resemble one another and give them a common name. The universal is no more than the name.

The *conceptualist* differs only slightly from the nominalist. He holds that there *are* universals, but that they are made only by the mind. The universal for him is an intellectual construction which has no basis in things outside the mind. The nature, for the conceptualist, has no existence in the singular things. Like the nominalist, the conceptualist believes that we select a group of concrete objects and give them a common name, but he adds that we also form a concept, and this concept is the universal.

The *Thomist* on the other hand holds that the common nature belongs to the singulars in the real order. Our intellect has the power to *discern* the common nature in the singular objects. The nature exists as a universal in the mind, while in the singulars it has only an individual existence. Nature has various modes of existence indifferently. Though we know the nature as a universal in the conceptual order, yet the nature itself is in the real order with an individual existence in the particular objects of which it is affirmed. What the mind contemplates is the nature. The concept is that *in which* it knows the nature.

At the other end of the scale the *extreme realists* hold that not only is there a universal, but that it has an existence outside the mind independent of the particulars.

In contradistinction to the doctrines of the extreme realists, of the nominalists, and of the conceptualists, the universal for the Thomist exists only in the mind, but it *has* a foundation in the real order.

### Universals and Artifacts

Having reached this point we may go on to ask : Is it not possible further for the mind artificially to manufacture to itself something, which has an analogy to a concept, formed by an arbitrary grouping of objects ? This concept-by-analogy of our own creation, however, will certainly not be a true universal, since it does not transcend the particular.

Alternatively, is it not the case that we can, if we so please, group together arbitrarily a number of objects under one name ?

To assert that we have the power to perform either or both of these operations is not to propound a philosophical conceptualism or nominalism as a theory of universals. We must carefully dissociate the present doctrine from that of the conceptualists and nominalists, who, perhaps, noticing these activities of the human mind, mistakenly thought that they provided an insight into the nature and origin of universals.

The sort of concept-by-analogy we are concerned with here is what we have called an 'artifact' since it is made artificially by man and does not come from Nature.

When we are considering an object there is to start with the real nature of the object. This is the case for any object. But we are not *obliged* to consider the object always under this aspect. We may, if we please, abstract from the real nature, and consider the object under some more artificial aspect, perhaps in some conventional and arbitrary association with a number of other objects. *This is not to deny in any way the real nature of the objects. It is merely that we are not now concerned with them under that aspect.*

It may clarify the situation to discuss the matter in terms of Plato's doctrine of universals. Let us consider the case Plato discusses in Book X of the *Republic*, that of a bed.[1] It is quite apparent that where what we call a bed leaves off and a sofa or a hammock, etc., commences, is an arbitrary and conventional matter. While it is perfectly true that each bed has a real nature which makes it what it is, yet we may not be particularly concerned with this. The furniture manufacturer may be more concerned with grouping together a number of objects more or less according to the prevailing convention, and attaching thereto the label ' bed.' What is relevant to the furniture manufacturer is the group separated out under a common name ; or alternatively we might say he has formed the artificial 'concept' of a bed at the dictates of convention. This, of course, is not a real universal concept, but is a concept by analogy.

Thus we could discuss beds under the aspect of an eternal form of a bed, as Plato does in the *Republic*. Or we could discuss beds practically as a conventional group. These are *not* two mutually exclusive operations : they are alternative.

### Univocal and Equivocal Terms

The Scholastic logician is concerned with the real universal i.e. with the concept in which the nature is known. The name or term for the Scholastic is a word which signifies the concept and, through the concept, the objects of that concept.

If attention is drawn to the fact that the intension and extension of such a term as 'bed' is determined by convention and changes from time to time, the Scholastic logician tends to reply that what a term *signifies* is indeed a matter of convention. A term which is used with different meanings, i.e. different intensions, is called by him an *equivocal term*. Consequently

[1] cf. p. 125.

the fact that the term 'bed' is used conventionally to apply to a different range of objects at different times, indicates to the Scholastic logician merely that the term 'bed' is equivocal.

Similarly in another example we used, that of a charitable bequest,[1] the conventional character of its intension tells us nothing more than that 'charitable bequest' is an equivocal term, so far as the Scholastic logician is concerned.

This is quite proper from the point of view of Scholastic logic. But what of the alternative artificial way of looking at the matter which we have suggested?

Instead of considering the real universals and equivocal terms, we may, if we please, consider the matter under the other aspect. We may discuss beds merely under the aspect of a conventional group. It is when we do this that we enter the realm of what we called the 'categorial logic,' a realm which we have already discussed in some detail.[2]

### Erroneous Hypostatisation

*This categorial 'logic' is a logic by analogy.* The categorial logic has its own laws, which we saw were generally describable as sociological. But, of course, it is not a *real* logic. There is only one real logic. However, the categorial may be fairly described as logic by analogy.

This categorial doctrine, as we have said, bears a close formal resemblance to conceptualism and nominalism. *But it differs from these in recognising that the system is artificial, and not real. Conceptualism and nominalism are our categorial hypostatised.*

The modern logicians, whose work we have described as categorial, have for the most part themselves hypostatised the system, i.e. they have made the same error as the nominalists and conceptualists. They have mistaken an artifact for an object of Nature. But the fact that they have erred does not justify our throwing the baby out with the bath water. We can retain the substance of their laborious work as an artificial structure, a logic by analogy.

[1] Ch. VIII.
[2] Ch. VIII.

*The raison d'être of Artifact Systems*

And now we might ask what is the purpose of reverting from real logic to this artificial aspect of things? The answer in a general way is that for some purposes it is convenient so to do.

For instance, in an ideal state positive law and natural law would enjoy a perfect harmony.[1] There would, in principle, be no need to consider anything but the real order, and no need to revert to anything but the Thomist logic.

But in actual states the positive law may possess only a loose connection with the natural law. Our example of the charitable bequest[2] indicated that in the legal order the jurist will be required to look to the conventions of society, and not, as a moralist would, to the real order. In an actual state there may even be a conflict between the jurist and the moralist. The Scholastic philosopher describes this state of affairs by saying that terms are equivocal. But this is somewhat remote from the practical requirements of the situation. Here the categorial 'logician' steps in and points out how the structure of the legal order in itself may very conveniently be described in terms of the categorial 'logic' and its laws. This is not in any way to deny the Scholastic view. It is merely to show the practical convenience of an artificial scheme.

It is the mistake of so many modern philosophers to regard practical convenience, and devices to further it, as being the very reality itself. We have already seen examples of this in other fields, e.g. hypostatising the entities of modern physics instead of treating them as the artificial, but very useful, devices that they are; or again, hypostatising the entities of Freudian psychology, and so on.

If taking such artifacts for natural objects has deceived so many, it is not to be wondered at that recent logical writers have often mistaken the artifacts of categorial 'logic' for the real. When this mistake is rectified we are left with a very useful system which vastly simplifies many discussions.

We may anticipate that, as time goes on, there will be

[1] We have discussed this already in Ch. II.
[2] p. 118.

propounded a number of different systems of artifact logic, each with its own structure and laws. This multiplicity will correspond to the variety in other artifact systems, e.g. the many non-Euclidean geometries which have been proposed in modern times. The real order, by contrast, is always one and unchanging.

## Plato's Divided Line

In a general way we may say that the further we go down towards the bottom of Plato's divided line the less concerned we feel about real natures[1] (though, of course, they are still there) and the more concerned we are to speak with the categorial philosophers on their artificial plane.

Conversely, the higher we mount on Plato's divided line the more insistent do the real natures become, and the less important are categorial considerations.

We may delegate to Protagoras a certain supervision in the lower regions but he is powerless as we mount higher.

## The Philosophical and the Sociological

It is to be hoped that this will clear up any Scholastic difficulties about our doctrine of the two orders, the real and the categorial, or *physis* and *nomos*, to use the Greek antithesis. To recognise the element of *nomos* is not to deny the universality of the *physis*. It is merely to point out that things may be considered under one aspect in terms of *nomos*. It is an artificial mode of considering them, and yet it may be a very convenient mode.

*In this way we hold to the strict Scholastic logical doctrines, but yet we admit the modern movements as devices.*

We might express this as a distinction between *philosophical nominalism* and *sociological nominalism*, just as we previously drew a distinction between *philosophical atomism* and *scientific atomism*.[2]

We may accept scientific atomism as a device for practical purposes, while rejecting philosophical atomism as untenable.

---

[1] Plato, too, felt this. See *Parmenides* 130 c & d.
[2] See pp. 61 f.

The scientific atoms, while they have being in a sense in that they are objects talked about, etc., yet nevertheless have a very low ontological status. Similarly in our order of sociological nominalism or conceptualism the entities there discussed possess a very low order of being. The concepts are concepts only by analogy, they too enjoy only a very low ontological status.

We may set out these relations in a tabular form thus :

| The Real Order (Singular) | | The Categorial Order of Artifacts (Multiple) |
|---|---|---|
| Accepted | Rejected | Scientific (i.e. Procrustean) Atomism |
| Hylomorphism | Philosophical Atomism | |
| Real Natures | Philosophical : ⎰ Nominalism ⎱ Conceptualism | Sociological (i.e. categorial) : ⎰ Nominalism ⎱ Conceptualism |
| Euclidean Geometry | Philosophical : ⎧ Riemann Geometry ⎨ Lobatchewsky Geometry, etc. | Mathematical : ⎧ Riemann Geometry ⎨ Lobatchewsky Geometry, etc. |

The science of modern physics was born when we started to elaborate a Procrustean order in the natural world. Scientific atomism is a typical product of this activity.

Similarly we might associate the present interest in sociological pursuits and the elaboration of a sociological 'logic' with the attempt to develop an autonomous *science* of human affairs, as distinct from a *philosophy* of human affairs.

No doubt to an infinitely wise being who possessed a perfect knowledge of all real natures no further artifices would be required. Such a being would, by virtue of his knowledge, have perfect mastery over the world. But we have finite minds and a limited knowledge of real natures. (According to St. Thomas this inherent limitation was accentuated by man's capacity for sharing in the Divine Reason having been weakened by the Fall.) This limited knowledge does not suffice for more than a modicum of control over the world. *Men have come to learn how to increase this control, not by increasing their knowledge of real natures, as this is for the most part denied to them, but by elaborating an artificial world, or a categorial order, as we have called it, and by this means acquiring a manipulative control over their subject matter.*

It is because this categorial order is one of mental or sociological artifacts formed by abstracting from real natures, that it is autonomous, enjoying its own laws and properties. We saw previously how the autonomy of modern physics had for long puzzled the philosophers, and how the puzzle is resolved by pointing out the artificial nature of the world of modern physics.

Similarly in recent times the autonomy of many of the movements and theories in the broad realm of sociology tends to puzzle and elude philosophers of the *philosophia perennis*. But if the entities of these theories, in principle, are regarded not as in some way contradictory to the real, but as artifacts, then the puzzle disappears. Consequently we can have our social *sciences* proceeding autonomously without any conflict with social *philosophy*.

Many of the protagonists of modern physical science and social science mistakenly hypostatise their science and treat it as a physical or social *philosophy*. But this is quite a misunderstanding.

### The Doctrine of Ens Rationis

A doctrine in general conformity with our doctrine of the order of mental artifacts is actually to be found in the germ in the traditional logic.

Maritain, for instance, writes:

The mind does not only abstract from the sensible those

intelligible natures which are realised in the world of existence : it does not only set before itself those natures or the notions which are born from such, in consideration of the world of existence, all of which are able to exist : in brief, it does not only conceive of real beings, i.e. beings capable of existence, it can also construct in the image of such natures, *ad instar entis*, objects of thought *incapable of existing* outside the mind (e.g. gender and species, the subject, the predicate, etc.) which the ancients called rational beings, *entia rationis*.[1]

And he adds :

God does not make rational beings ; it is a mark of the weakness of our abstract intelligence that in so many cases it has no power to conform itself to reality except by constructing these rational beings.[2]

According to Maritain we find rational beings in a number of fields ; for instance, in addition to the examples already mentioned, in privations like evil and deafness; in such impossible entities as the square circle; in the fictions of mathematics; and even in the atoms and electrons of the physicists.

It will be apparent that what we have called artifacts include what the traditional logicians called *entia rationis*. But the field of artifacts covers a wider area than what has commonly been envisaged as the field of the *entia rationis*.

Artifacts, we have claimed, are the products of our categorial activities. These activities are to be found in well nigh every department, creating a series of shadowy secondary worlds. The doctrine of artifacts is then a development and extension of the classical doctrine of *entia rationis*.

## The Order of Artifacts and Morality

The elaboration and employment of mental artifacts is in itself amoral. But morality is involved as soon as the mode of employment of these artifact systems comes up for consideration.

The simplest case is that of modern physics.[3] The pursuit

[1] Maritain, J. : *The Degrees of Knowledge* (Eng. Tr.), (London, 1937), p. 160.
[2] *Ibid.* p. 162.
[3] cf. p. 58.

of modern physical science in itself is morally neutral, or perhaps we might say praiseworthy in that it is an exercise of our intellectual endowments. But when we come to applying physics in the world we are confronted with moral problems. We must make a moral decision about the ends to which our new powers are to be directed. Up to the present the ends have been quite fortuitous. The possession of such great powers is a standing challenge to the quality of our morality.

Similarly if a social science can be developed, i.e. a science of human affairs, this in itself is ethically neutral. But the moral issue arises as soon as we ask : To what ends are our new social powers to be directed ?

*Diagrammatic Representation*

The relations of the two orders may be represented diagrammatically thus :—

NATURAL ORDER
*Theocentric*

CATEGORIAL ORDER
{ *Anthropocentric*
{ *Sociocentric*

As a commentary on the Diagram let us quote from Jacques Lefèvre d'Étaples, a famous philosopher of the School of Paris, writing in 1503 on the subject of astronomical systems :

This part of astronomy is almost entirely an affair of representation and imagination. The very good and very wise Artisan of all things, by an operation of His divine intelligence, has produced the true skies and their true movements ; in the same way our intelligence composes in itself fictional skies and fictional movements; these are phantoms of the true skies and the true movements. . . . When the mind of the astronomer composes a precise representation of the skies and of their movements, it resembles the Artisan of all things, creating the skies and their movements.

## Summary

Quite enough has been said to illustrate and explain the doctrine of the two orders.

Post-Renaissance Procrustean physics is an extreme example of the working of the categorial order, or the order of artifacts.

In a looser form, the categorial order is found in almost every department of life: in speech, in the law courts, in modern logic, in the teachings of the Greek sophists, and so on.

The real order is embedded in the nature of the universe. Ultimately it is theocentric, being derived immediately from God.

The categorial order is man-made. It is egocentric, or more usually sociocentric, being derived immediately from man and society.

The two orders are properly complementary.

Man is the measure of all things, man is the monarch of all he surveys—up to a point. If he exceeds the mark the Erinyes will find him out.

## PART III

## SCHOLASTIC PHILOSOPHY AND MODERN PHYSICS

*A philosophy cannot be constructed from physics ; when a man who happens also to be a physicist writes meta-physics he is advocating views which lie outside the domain of scientific physics.*

ALFRED O'RAHILLY: *Electromagnetics.*

*The possibility of observation and measurement thus replaces for such forms of knowledge the essence or quiddity sought for in things by philosophy.*

JACQUES MARITAIN : *The Degrees of Knowledge.*

# CHAPTER XVII

# THE RISE OF THE NEW LEARNING

## The Clash of the Two Learnings

NO discussion of Scholastic Philosophy and Modern Physics could be fully intelligible without some reference to the history of the relations between the two. Accordingly in this chapter we will cast a backward glance to the discussions of former days. We will find them very instructive indeed.

The 17th century was on the whole violently anti-Aristotelean. The system of Aristotle was commonly believed to have been demolished to its foundations by the new sciences. Galileo himself, in his famous *Dialogues on the Two Great Systems of the World*, makes Sagredus say ironically of the Aristotelean system :

‘ Shall we overthrow that Fabrick under which so many passengers find shelter ? Shall we destroy that *Asylum*, that *Prytaneum*, wherein so many students meet with commodious harbour ? where without exposing themselves to the injuries of the air, with the only turning over of a few leaves, one may learn all the secrets of Nature ? Shall we dismantle that fort in which we are safe from all hostile assaults ? But I pity him no more than I do that Gentleman who, with great expense of time and treasure, and the help of many hundred artists, erects a very sumptuous Pallace, and afterwards beholds it ready to fall, by reason of the bad foundation ; but being extremely unwilling to see the walls stript which are adorned with so many beautiful pictures ; or to suffer the columns to fall, that uphold the stately galleries ; or the gilded roofs, chimney pieces, the friezes, the cornices of marble, with so much cost erected, to be ruined ; goeth about with girders, props, shoars, buttresses, to prevent their subversion.’[1]

[1] *Dialogue I.*   Thomas   Salusbury’s   translation   (1661) : (Spelling slightly modernised).

Much more extreme criticisms of the Aristotelean system and the Aristoteleans can be found in other writers of the period. But this from Galileo will suffice here.

While it is true that the rise of modern physics has occasioned the Scholastic philosophers a great amount of thought, yet the popular idea that the movement centring around Galileo spelt death to the old philosophy is in fact quite unfounded.

As we shall see presently, the relations between the two schools of thought have, on the whole, been quite friendly, at least as far as the philosopher is concerned. Unfortunately the physicist was sometimes rather hostile to the philosopher, mainly because of his, the physicist's, failure to appreciate the larger issues confronting the philosopher.

It is significant that the Church, the patron of the *philosophia perennis*, was, and ever continued to be, a patron too of the new scientific learning. Collisions sometimes occurred, but these belonged to the realm of accident, not of essence. They were due for the most part to the extra-scientific activities of the scientist. In so far as the scientist, *qua* scientist, confined his authority to his science, the Church looked upon his activities with approval and encouragement. But scientists, with a natural but misguided enthusiasm, not infrequently tend to intrude into the realms of philosophy and religion. These are subtle and rigorous fields for which the scientist rarely has any special aptitude, and into which his intrusion is only too often merely mischievous. The rigours of his professional training rarely leave the natural scientist the leisure thoroughly to master the no less exacting pursuits of the philosophical and theological sciences.

When irresponsible and harmful intrusions occur it is clearly the Church's duty to discourage them.

This led e.g. to the famous incident of the condemnation of Galileo. It is the only clash of any significance which occurred between the Church and the new scientific schools. It has been magnified by controversy, and has come to assume the dimensions of a *cause célèbre*. This condemnation sprang, not from the *practice* of the new science, which was not really in dispute, but rather, as we shall see presently, from Galileo's co-lateral opinions in philosophy and theology. That the Church was not opposed to the new science as such, is borne out by the fact that Church scholars, notably the Jesuit professors, were among the foremost exponents in Europe of the new learning.[1]

To trace in detail the relationship between the scientists on the one hand, and the Scholastics and the Church on the other, would be an interesting and enlightening task. But it would lead us too far afield to be dealt with in this work. Here we shall confine ourselves to a few representative opinions and theories.

### St. Thomas Aquinas

Although St. Thomas lived long before the rise of modern physics, yet even in his day there were disputes in astronomy which needed some comment.[2] The orthodox peripatetics defended Aristotle's astronomy with its contention that all the heavenly bodies travelled with a uniform circular motion. But the erratic behaviour of the planets had led to the emendation of Aristotle by Hipparchus and later by Ptolemy. Thus arose the famous theory of cycles and epicycles in the heavens. By this theory it was possible to give a satisfactory account of the observed heavenly motions.

On this subject St. Thomas writes[3] :

The suppositions which astronomers have imagined are not to be accounted necessarily true. Although these hypotheses seem

---

[1] Popular history, even to the present day, gives but a distorted view of the period. J. Brodrick in his *Progress of the Jesuits* (London, 1946), pp. 102-3 n., gives a typical instance, from no less a work than Fisher's *History of Europe*, where the dead weight of inherited prejudice led the author unwittingly into an almost comic blunder. Few, if any, of the commonly accessible accounts of 17th century thought do anything like justice to all parties.

[2] We shall consider the various theories on this matter current in the ancient and medieval world in more detail in the Appendix.

[3] *Expositio super Libro de Caelo et Mundo.* Quoted by J. Brodrick : *Life and Work of Cardinal Bellarmine* (London, 1928), *v.* 2, p. 330. Subsequent references here to Brodrick are to this work : Ch. XXVI ' *The First Troubles of Galileo.*' The whole of this chapter should be read for the clear light it throws on the thought of the times at the birth of the new sciences.

to save the appearances,[1] we must not say that they are thereby proved to be facts, because perhaps it would be possible to explain the apparent movements of the stars by some other method which men have not yet excogitated.

This principle, endorsed by St. Thomas, that the particular theories of scientists should not be taken too literally, but rather with a certain amount of caution, might well be taken as a text on which to hang much of the subsequent history of Scholastic thought on the subject. It hints at a slight cleavage between a particular physical theory and what actually is the case. This principle, very much developed, is one of the main contentions of the present work.

### Cardinal Bellarmine and Galileo

The Copernican theory, that it is the Sun which is stationary and the Earth which moves, was taken up and greatly developed and hotly championed by that remarkable man Galileo Galilei. The new system of the world aroused immense interest throughout Europe. It was denounced off-hand by some, such as Martin Luther, on the grounds that it was contrary to Scripture.[2] In learned Catholic circles it gained wide acceptance,[3] although there was some uneasiness on the question of Scriptural reconciliation.

Galileo himself in 1613 wrote a letter to one of his pupils, the Benedictine Benedetto Castelli, on the subject of the new astronomy and Scriptural exegesis[4] in which he says :

Since, then, the Holy Scriptures not only admit but require in many places a different explanation from that which appears to be the obvious meaning of the words, it seems to me that they ought to be reserved for the last place in scientific discussions. . . . It seems to me that no effect of nature which our sense experience places before our eyes or which is a necessary conclusion from our experience, ought to be called in question on the strength of Scripture texts which seem to imply the contrary, because not every

---

[1] A common phrase during the early period of modern science. It is equivalent to ' accounting for the observed facts ' or some such expression.

[2] Brodrick, *ibid.* p. 331.

[3] e.g. Pope Gregory XIII in 1582 reformed the calendar using Tables based on the Copernican system.

[4] Quoted by Brodrick, *ibid.* pp. 349 f.

saying of Scripture is bound by such rigid laws as is every effect of nature. . . . Since it is plain that two truths can never contradict each other, it is the duty of wise interpreters to take the pains to find out the real meaning of the sacred texts, in accordance with those conclusions of natural science which the clear evidence of the senses, or apodeictic demonstrations, have put beyond dispute. . . .[1]

Brodrick points out how sound are the principles laid down in this letter of Galileo's concerning the interpretation of Scripture. But he wisely adds[2]:

In dealing with this matter it is necessary in justice to all who were concerned to call attention to one great fallacy latent in the letter. Galileo gave it as his opinion that no effect of nature of which the senses afford evidence, or which is a necessary deduction from their evidence, should be considered doubtful because the Scriptures seemed to teach the contrary. In this opinion he was perfectly justified, but to imply, as he unquestionably did, that Copernicanism was a *necessary* deduction from the evidence of the senses, was to make his own genius, which had jumped to that conclusion, the standard for the rest of the world.[3]

---

[1] Galileo developed these ideas at greater length in 1615, in a letter to the Grand Duchess Christina Lotharinga. This letter contains his considered opinion on a difficult subject.

[2] Brodrick, *ibid.* p. 351.

[3] Has history anything more ironical to offer than the present-day fate of the great controversy of Copernicus *v.* Ptolemy, the one maintaining that the Earth moves, the other that it is stationary at the centre of the universe? For the publication of Einstein's *General Theory of Relativity* in 1916 (foreshadowed thirty years before by Ernst Mach), shows that *from the point of view of contemporary physical science* the dispute is an empty one, being simply a matter of whether we select a frame of reference fixed with respect to the Sun or one fixed with respect to the Earth. This choice is quite arbitrary and is dictated merely by convenience.

N.B.—The significance of Mach-Einstein relativity is not always understood. It goes far beyond mere *kinematic* or *geometrical* relativity, which has been clearly recognised at least since the days of Aristotle. Mach-Einstein relativity goes further, it is a *dynamical* relativity. On the Newtonian mechanics the hypothetical bucket at the North Pole, the Foucault pendulum, and so on, demonstrate the *absolute* rotation of the Earth in space. On the new system such experiments demonstrate only *relative* rotation between Earth and fixed stars, thus dissolving the Newtonian judgment on the ancient controversy. See Ernst Mach : *The Science of Mechanics*, Eng. Tr. (London, 1902), pp. 231 f. and pp. 542 f. Also A. Einstein : *The Foundation of the General Theory of Relativity* (London, 1920).

To assert the *absolute* truth of the Copernican system of the Universe, as such truth is understood in physical science, is thus possible only within the framework of Newtonian dynamics. Galileo, in the pre-Newtonian era, could thus have no valid proof of the Copernican system. From this point of view all his supposed proofs are illusory.

A year or two after this letter of Galileo's on astronomy and the Scriptures, Cardinal Bellarmine[1] had occasion to make a few remarks on the subject in a latter to a Carmelite Father, Foscarini, the author of a work defending the Copernican theory, who had sent him a copy and asked his opinion.    This letter of Bellarmine's may be taken to represent the mature Scholastic thought of the time, and in fact we find little that improves upon it right up to our own day, and, alas, much that falls below it.[2]

Bellarmine writes[3] :

It seems to me that your Reverence and Signor Galileo would act prudently were you to content yourselves with speaking hypothetically and not absolutely, as I have always believed that Copernicus spoke.[4]    To say that on the supposition of the earth's movement and the sun's quiescence all the celestial appearances are explained better than by the theory of eccentrics and epicycles, is to speak with excellent good sense and to run no risk whatever. Such a manner of speaking is enough for a mathematician.    But to want to affirm that the sun, in very truth, is at the centre of the universe and only rotates on its axis without going from east to west, is a very dangerous attitude and one calculated not only to annoy all scholastic philosophers and theologians but also to injure our holy faith by contradicting the Scriptures. . . .    If there were a real proof that the sun is in the centre of the universe, that the earth is in the third heaven, and that the sun does not go round the earth but the earth round the sun, then we should have to proceed with great circumspection in explaining passages of Scripture which appear to teach the contrary, and rather admit that we did not understand them than declare an opinion to be false which is proved to be true.    But as for myself, I shall not believe that there

---

[1] Now Saint Robert Bellarmine.    He was, incidentally, one of the ' qualifiers ' of the Holy Office which in 1616 condemned the heliocentric theory as taught by Galileo.

[2] These reflections of Bellarmine's are not isolated ; on the contrary they represent a mature tradition (see Appendix).

[3] Quoted by Brodrick, *op. cit.* p. 358.    This letter was first published in 1876 at Rome.

[4] This belief was based on the Preface to Copernicus' *De revolutionibus*, which Preface, it now appears, was not written by Copernicus at all, but was inserted by his editor, Andreas Osiander.    It is an interesting document and may be read in an English translation in *Three Copernican Treatises*, tr. Edward Rosen (Oxford, 1940).

are such proofs until they are shown to me. *Nor is a proof that, if the sun be supposed at the centre of the universe and the earth in the third heaven, the celestial appearances are thereby explained, equivalent to a proof that the sun actually is in the centre and the earth in the third heaven.* The first kind of proof might, I believe, be found, but as for the second kind, I have the very gravest doubts, and in case of doubt we ought not to abandon the interpretation of the sacred text as given by the holy fathers.

This is an eminently reasonable and conciliatory letter, and makes incipiently the distinction of the two orders which we have designated as the real and the categorial in discussing the character of modern physical science.[1] Galileo knew of Bellarmine's letter, but specifically rejected its proposals. Had he been prepared to fall in with Bellarmine's principles there need have been no conflict with the Holy Office (see Appendix).

### The Seventeenth Century

Had more heed been paid to men like Cardinal Bellarmine the new astronomy and the new physics could easily have been subsumed into the Scholastic philosophy of the world.[2] True, many of the more specifically *scientific* theories of Aristotle and the Scholastics would have had to be modified, starting with some aspects of the geocentric theory. But the Scholastic metaphysics would have been quite unaffected, resting as it does, not on particular physical theories, but on the most general and universal principles, which are quite independent of particular theories.[3] Hence it is true up to a point that even for the Aristoteleans the science of Nature is one thing and the philosophy of Nature is another. The particular theories of the science of Nature are ever varying, keeping pace with 'saving the appearances.' The philosophy of Nature is eternal.

Copernicus, Tycho Brahe, Kepler, Galileo, Newton, and all

[1] See Ch. III.

[2] Recent researches into the long-neglected Scholastics of the 14th century, such as Buridan, have shown that much of the new learning was foreshadowed in the Schools.

[3] See p. 54, n. 1.

the rest of the shining pantheon of the 17th century could have been absorbed peacefully. But the spirit of the times was one of violent reaction, and Aristotle and all his works were consigned to the flames, metaphorically at least. Instead of distinguishing the small non-essential part which had become doubtful from the great fundamental part which remained true, the whole work of Aristotle and the Schoolmen was treated with equal contempt.

Galileo, in popular thought, became the knight in shining armour who rescued the world from the long night of the 'Dark Ages.' Although this is a fantastic travesty of history it persists right down to the present day, and is still the staple diet provided in scientific text books. The Church, too, as well as the philosophers, shares in the general obloquy because Galileo was brought before the Inquisition.

From the 17th century onwards there has been a Babel of conflicting voices attempting to fill the void left by the suppression of Scholasticism. The hapless pilgrim today will look in vain for any sure path through the tortuous maze of modern philosophies. Fr. Clarke remarks rather aptly in his *Logic*:

One philosophy after another rises up in modern days and proclaims itself to be the voice of a teacher sent from God. For a time its prophet gathers round himself a number of enthusiastic disciples, and promises great things to an unenlightened world. But soon a rival appears, and denounces his predecessor as inconsistent with himself and inconsistent with Truth, and engages to remedy the evil by fresh discoveries of its own. But alas! the promise is but ill fulfilled ; he, too, is slain in his turn by one who follows close upon his heels, and who denounces him with no less vigour than he had himself displayed against his discarded predecessor.

This account of the vain succession of modern philosophers, each driving out his predecessor, is reminiscent of Frazer's moving account in *The Golden Bough* of the terrible priesthood at Lake Nemi in the Alban Hills, where the rule was that each occupant of the office was to be slain and his place taken by the slayer, only for him to be slain in his turn, and so on indefinitely.

Fr. Clarke goes on:

Thus it is that the battle goes on continually outside the Catholic Church, and the internecine warfare is mistaken for a healthy sign of life. The multiformity of error is misnamed the many-sidedness of truth, and even when one hypothesis after another proves to be utterly untenable, men are content to invent yet another that it too may be rejected in its turn.[1]

## The Leonine Revival

Even in orthodox ecclesiastical circles the Scholastic philosophy fell somewhat into abeyance during the centuries following the rise of the new sciences. But a revival commenced in the latter part of the 19th century. The revival received a great impetus from the Encyclical of Leo XIII, *Aeterni Patris*, published in 1879, which enjoined the restoration of philosophy after the manner of St. Thomas Aquinas. This encyclical inaugurated the 'neo-Scholastic' era.

Since that time much has been written on the subject of Scholastic philosophy and the new learning, prominent in which is of course modern physics.

As regards modern physics, several schools of thought have appeared.

Some neo-Scholastics have thought it necessary to make substantial alterations in Scholastic principles in order to bring them into line with modern science. This is more than merely modifying particular doctrines of the Aristotelean *science of Nature* of the Middle Ages (many of which doctrines were really incidental to the *philosophy*). It means altering the principles of the *philosophy of Nature*.

Alternatively, some have given novel interpretations to the current principles of physical science, to make them fit more easily into the scheme of Aristotelean principles.

All such philosophers we might call the '*Scholastic Unifiers*' since they seek in some way to make a direct union between modern science and philosophy, and weld them into one whole.

But the greater number of neo-Scholastics have believed that no alteration in philosophical principles is warranted, or

[1] Clarke, R. F. : *Logic*, pp. 481–2.

is indeed possible, and have rather pursued the line suggested so long ago by Cardinal Bellarmine : that there are two orders, the one scientific, the other philosophical or ontological. The scientific order is autonomous and is rightly left entirely in the hands of the scientists themselves, provided that, *qua* scientists, they confine themselves to that order.

Philosophers who follow this path we might call the ' *Scholastic Dualists*', since they envisage two orders.

Precisely what is the character of this scientific order, and how it is related to the philosophical order, is a matter of much debate. We will subsequently examine some representative modern views, and show how they culminate in the categorial theory of modern physics, already discussed in this work. (Ch. III).

A modern writer, R. P. Phillips, in his *Modern Thomistic Philosophy*,[1] justly describes this whole subject as one of great difficulty and importance, and one the complete solution of which cannot be found in the writings of St. Thomas. He draws attention cogently to the similarity between this situation today and that which confronted St. Thomas in the 13th century. St. Thomas' task was to unite the purely rational philosophy of Aristotle, newly reintroduced into Europe, with the structure of Christian theology. The *Summa Theologica* contains the synthesis worked out well nigh to the last detail. Our task in the 20th century is to carry on the Thomist synthesis and harmonise modern physical science with the Scholastic world order.

Modern Thomist approaches to this synthesis are largely built on current theories about the nature of physical science. The Unifiers and the Dualists base themselves on different views of the nature of modern physics. Hence before discussing the neo-Thomist theories it will be as well to summarise very briefly what the physicists have thought about their science.

---

[1] (London, 1934), *v.* 2, p. 144.

# CHAPTER XVIII

# THEORIES OF EMPIRICAL SCIENCE

HERE we must needs recapitulate something of the introduction to Ch. III, and at the same time make the situation more specific.

The various philosophies of physical science have an interesting history. We can only summarise them here.

## The Realist Theory

As we remarked in Ch. III, the proponents of the new science of physics, ever since the 17th century, have almost unanimously contended in a dogmatic fashion that their science was telling us about the real nature of the world, that it was in some way a philosophy of the world, or at least was closely connected with such a philosophy, and that it made the Aristotelean philosophy untenable. Instead of Aristotelean philosophy some other philosophy must be evolved, they believed, grounded on, or at least conformable to, the world of modern physics. Just *what* this philosophy should be, however, was always a matter of contention.

Alternatively, some contended naïvely that philosophy was defunct, and that the only true knowledge was that of natural science.

As a corollary to this point of view, it was widely held that with the progress of science would come ever greater knowledge and wisdom about the world. The progress of science it was believed, is, in principle, the progress of mankind. If this conjunction does not in fact appear, then, so it was held, the cause must lie in the misapplication of our scientific knowledge, or in the resistance offered to its diffusion by the forces of obscurantism and reaction.

It would be difficult to estimate how large a part this notion has played in the last two or three centuries in semi-popular, and even learned circles, in forming the prevailing thought of the times.   It is one of the main springs of 'liberal' thought.

As far as the scientists themselves are concerned, the 'realist' theory itself was practically unchallenged from the 17th century until modern times.   Illustrations could be drawn from innumerable authors.

It will be sufficient here to quote Sir Isaac Newton, who stands like a Colossus astride the medieval and modern worlds. He is the prototype of the later physical realists.   It never occurred to Newton to doubt the reality and objectivity of the world of mathematical physics of which he was such a master.   To Newton, space, time, mass, gravitation, etc. were the very stuff of which the world was made.   Newton, as well as being a mathematical physicist, was also a keen theologian.   He wrote widely on theological subjects.   But he probably felt that these were not two different pursuits at all.   They were for him, on the contrary, one and the same pursuit.   When Newton was investigating absolute space and absolute time he believed that he was pursuing natural theology. For, to him, absolute space and absolute time were attributes or properties of God.

He explains his ideas about God in the General Scholium at the end of the Second Edition of the *Principia*.   The passage is too long to quote in full, but a few extracts will make his outlook intelligible :

This most beautiful system of the sun, planets, and comets, could only proceed from the counsel and dominion of an intelligible and powerful Being. . . .   This Being governs all things, not as the soul of the world, but as Lord over all ; and on account of his dominion he is wont to be called *Lord God.* . . .   He is eternal and infinite, omnipotent and omniscient; that is, his duration reaches from eternity to eternity ; his presence from infinity to infinity ; he governs all things, and knows all things that are or can be done. He is not eternity and infinity, but eternal and infinite ; he is not duration or space, but he endures and is present.   He endures forever, and is everywhere present; and *by existing always and everywhere he constitutes duration and space. . . .* And thus much concerning God; to discourse of whom from the appearances of things, does certainly belong to Natural Philosophy.'[1]

Now, let us couple these views on natural theology with the programme of mathematical physics laid down at the beginning of the *Principia*. There he states the doctrine of absolute time and absolute space, speaks of the difficulty of arriving at them, because, *prima facie*, our senses tell us only of relative time and space, and concludes with these significant words.[2]

But how we are to obtain the true motions from their causes, effects, and apparent differences, and the converse, shall be explained more at large in the following treatise. *For to this end it was that I composed it.*

He composed the *Principia*, then, primarily to explain how to arrive at absolute space and time. And absolute space and time are for him essentially connected with God's nature.

It would be difficult indeed to separate Newton the physicist from Newton the theologian.[3]

Even today many, perhaps the majority, of physicists subscribe to much the same 'realist' interpretation of the world of physics, with or without the theological implications (usually without). They take the physical picture of the world quite literally. For them, atoms, electrons, gravitation, etc. are really 'there' just as much as chairs and tables.

This belief is sometimes the starting point of a chain of reflection which leads to a philosophy of materialism. This is a doctrine which was very popular in the 19th century.

---

[1] These quotations are from pp. 544–546 of the splendid edition of Newton's *Principia*, edited, in English, by Florian Cajori (Cambridge, 1934).

[2] *Ibid.* p. 12.

[3] We can hardly leave this aspect of Newton's intellectual system without pointing out how completely Immanuel Kant, a century after the publication of the *Principia*, was to reverse the situation on this precise point. From Newton to Kant is certainly a Copernican revolution. For Newton absolute space and time were objective, and, indeed, virtually attributes of the deity. For Kant not only were they not attributes of God, they were not even objective, but instead were two pure forms of sensible intuition. He writes :

' Space does not represent any property of things in themselves, nor does it represent them in their relation to one another.'

Similarly:

' Time is not something which exists of itself, or which inheres in things as an objective determination.' (Kant : *Critique of Pure Reason*, B 42 and B 49).

Sometimes, on the contrary, it leads to a theism of one kind or another. For instance recently the late Sir James Jeans argued from the mathematical structure of modern physics to the existence of God as a great mathematician.

The realist interpretation of physics lends itself in fact to practically any conclusions about the universe. Physicists can usually conclude to anything which, on other grounds, they have a pre-disposition to believe.[1]

## The Phenomenalist Theory

In the last half century or so the realist school of thought has been receding, and the rival phenomenalist theory has been gaining more and more adherents.

This phenomenalist theory received a great impetus from the brilliant writings of Ernst Mach.[2] In his epoch-making *Die Mechanik in ihrer Entwickelung*, first published in 1883, he held that the function of physical science is merely to give the most economical description of empirical phenomena. In direct contradiction to the realists, he held that entities such as atoms, far from being real, are merely mental artifices for facilitating the mental reproduction of facts.[3]

Like the realist theory, Mach's phenomenalist theory is a *passive* theory, i.e. it holds that the physicist passively receives phenomena. The realists believe that we deduce thence the real structure of the objective physical world. The phenomenalists deny that we can move beyond the phenomena, except, as Mach allows, that we can construct mental artifices, or mnemonics, to tie together groups of phenomena.[4]

---

[1] See pp. 55 f.

[2] In the Appendix we will discuss philosophers of the later Middle Ages who held similar theories to Mach's. But their work had been forgotten.

[3] See e.g. pp. 491 f. of the English Translation.

[4] It will be apparent that the passive phenomenalist school of thought is a continuation of English Empiricism of the type of Locke, Berkeley, and Hume. Mach's emendation, that we can construct mental artifices as an aid, seems to be the gist of the recent elaborate and amusing arguments of John Wisdom in his article ' Other Minds,' *Mind*, 1940, pp. 369 f. (See Ch. V).

Professor Herbert Dingle in his interesting book : *Through Science to Philosophy* (Oxford, 1937) has developed this phenomenalist theme over the whole range of modern physics.

The general tenor of the phenomenalist school is that we cannot find out anything about the nature of the world, if there be any, underlying the phenomena. We cannot pursue causes. Indeed strict phenomenalists would deny the reality of causation, and would claim that there is nothing more than observed sequences of events. This leads readily into a philosophy of positivism, or agnosticism, or idealism, or finally mysticism, according to taste.

As distinct from the foregoing *passive* phenomenalism, there has more recently grown up an *active* phenomenalism. The various exponents of this theory agree that the physicist deals in a way with phenomena, but they deny that the physicist merely passively receives the phenomena. They hold that the physicist himself in some way moulds and shapes the phenomena. The world of physics is indeed a mental artifice, but it is much more artificial than even Mach thought. For now it is not based on immediate objective phenomena passively received, but on transformed and highly sophisticated data. *The data of the physicists are not simply phenomena.*

The great exponent of this *active* phenomenalism is of course Professor Eddington, with his Procrustean theory of physics, which we have discussed in some detail in Ch. III.[1]

## Passive and Active Phenomenalism

The orthodox realist school of thought, which takes the world of physics quite literally, holds that there is only *one order* and that empirical science gives us our only knowledge of it.

The *passive* phenomenalist school, which regards the world of physics not as real, but as a mental artifice, likewise holds that there is only one order, or at least only one accessible to

---

[1] The precursor of Eddington is H. Poincaré whose views we have mentioned already (Ch. VII).

A contemporary American physicist whose views bear some resemblance to the active phenomenalist school of thought is P. W. Bridgman. In his *Logic of Modern Physics* (London, 1927) he maintains that a concept in physics should not be defined in terms of its properties, for then there is no assurance that there really exists in Nature anything with the properties assumed in the definition. On the contrary, he goes on, a concept means nothing more than a set of operations. It is in fact *synonymous* with the set of operations.

us, and that again empirical science gives us our only knowledge of it. The world underlying the phenomena is, like Kant's 'thing-in-itself,' quite unknown to us.

However, with *active* phenomenalism the situation is different. We may hold the Procrustean transformation in physics to be *voluntary* or *compulsory*. If the latter, i.e. if we hold that we *must* approach the world with the Procrustean transformation, that the only knowledge we *can* have of the world is by means of a Procrustean phenomenalism, then we are in much the same position as the passive phenomenalists. For once again the the world behind the phenomena is unknowable, so we go on either to deny that there is any underlying real world, and so slide into positivism, or we assert that there is a real world but we cannot know what it is, and so become agnostics, or at the best mystics.

Most exponents of active phenomenalism, like Eddington and Poincaré, have in fact held the theory in this compulsory form, with its corollary that there is only one accessible order.

*But we may hold the Procrustean theory of physics without believing the Procrustean transformation of the world to be compulsory and inescapable.* We may hold, on the contrary, that this transformation is *voluntary*, that it is a transformation we effect when we want to have an instrument not for 'knowing' but for 'doing.' We are quite capable of knowing the real world as it is without any transformation. Its transformation is something we can perform at will, and in no way prevents our knowledge of the real untransformed world.

This active phenomenalism, regarded as of voluntary application, admits of *two orders, both knowable*. In passive phenomenalism the phenomena arise immediately out of whatever real world there is, and we have no communication with the real world except through these phenomena. However, on the Procrustean theory the world of physics does not arise immediately from the real world. It is, on the contrary, the real world transformed at the dictates of the physicist in order that the physicist may increase his control.[1]

---

[1] i.e., as we cannot stress too much, the *data* of the physicists are not the *phenomena* of the Empiricist philosophers. This is a most important distinction.

As we have held throughout this work, the Procrustean transformation is not compulsory, we can if we choose approach the real world directly without subjecting it to the Procrustean transformation. The Procrustean approach is optional and is reserved for a special purpose namely, to gain control. Consequently we have two orders and both of them knowable.

The fact that modern exponents, like Eddington, have supposed that the transformations are inescapable, so that there is only one order, is a private idiosyncrasy of their own, and is not essential to their basic doctrine of the activity of the physicist. Their assumption of inescapability is similar to that made by Kant, that the categories are innate in the understanding. It was this assumption which ultimately wrecked Kant's system.

In the situation as we have expounded it the world of physics and the real world are at the second remove from one another. Thus the physical world has gained its immediate autonomy from the real world. Conversely, independent reflections on the real world by the philosopher can proceed without reference to the theories of modern physics, because of the separation of the orders. In passive phenomenalism, and likewise in compulsory active phenomenalism, any independent investigation would be impossible because of the immediate link.

Our voluntary Procrustean phenomenalism translates the physicist to an autonomous order, and both he and the philosopher can proceed without collision.

The conclusion, then, is that the realists and the passive phenomenalists tie up metaphysics and physics into one whole to the embarrassment of both, while our voluntary active phenomenalism cuts them asunder and allows each to develop according to its proper nature.

To sum up : As related in Ch. III, from an internal examination of the structure, procedure, and history of modern physics, we are led to the active Procrustean theory of physics. Further reflection shows that this process is not compulsory, but voluntary. Consequently we have a clear separation of the physicist and the metaphysician, and we see how each can operate autonomously.   In this way we finally remove the embarrassing liaison between the two, a supposed liaison which has been a thorn in the flesh of the *philosophia perennis* since the rise of modern physics in the 17th century.[1]

With this theoretical background we can now go on to examine the various schools of thought amongst the modern Scholastic philosophers.

We shall find the scholastic 'Unifiers' adhering to the orthodox 'realist' interpretation, taking the theories and entities of the physicists literally.

On the other hand the ' Dualists ' adhere more to the phenomenalist interpretation in one form or another.

Let us now consider these schools in turn.

---

[1] The great, but almost universally unrecognised contributions which Kant made to this *dénouement*, we have already pointed out (Ch. VI).   There is no need to revert to it here since this chapter is mainly historical and Kant, unfortunately, has had little or no influence on philosophical history in this particular topic.   Suffice it to say that the Scholastic revival might have come much earlier if the basic significance of the Kantian principles of physics had been recognised. However, that it was not recognised, it must be admitted, is largely Kant's own fault, since in an excess of zeal he overlaid his principle with so much indefensible superstructure.

# CHAPTER XIX

# THE SCHOLASTIC UNIFIERS

*Hylosystemism*

THIS is a system propounded in some neo-Scholastic circles in recent years in opposition to the traditional hylomorphism of Aristotle and St. Thomas in the explanation of the essential constitution of inorganic bodies.[1] It is founded on a consideration of the theories of modern physics relating to the nature of matter and the structure of the atom. It accepts the now somewhat old-fashioned 'realist' doctrine that the picture of the world given by modern physics is to be taken quite literally, that atoms, electrons, etc., are really ' there,' and are not merely mental artifices, as the phenomenalist school asserts.

A detailed discussion of hylosystemism *v.* hylomorphism may safely be left to works entering in a more detailed manner into Scholastic philosophy than the present. However, in view of the fact that the starting point of hylosystemism is the theories of modern physics, the significance of which has already been considered in this work, it may not be out of place to make a few observations here on hylosystemism.

According to the traditional theory of hylomorphism all natural bodies consist of a union of two principles: primary matter and substantial form. However, according to modern scientific research, the constitution of natural bodies is quite otherwise: matter is atomic in structure, and furthermore an atom consists of a dynamical system of a number of different kinds of particles: protons, neutrons, and electrons. The

---

[1] An account of this topic, in English, will be found in Bittle, C. N.: *From Ether to Cosmos*, Ch. XIV.

protons and the neutrons together form the nucleus of the atom and the electrons revolve around the nucleus in various orbits.

This is the Rutherford-Bohr model of the atom, which has generally been accepted in essentials for the last thirty years.[1] Associated with the atom in atomic phenomena, but not explicitly constituents of the atom, are other particles : the positive electron, the neutrino, the meson ; and in addition quanta.

For the purposes of philosophical discussion these particles have been called 'hylons,' and the exponents of 'hylosystemism,' take these particles to have a real existence. The peculiarity of the hylons is that they do not possess a full separate independent existence, but tend rather to unite in systems to form elementary bodies. According to the Thomists every body is a material substance, and *vice versa*. But now we have entities, hylons, which are material substances but not true bodies.

According to Bittle :

*hylomorphism* explains the composite substance of the natural body by means of *primary matter* and *substantial form*. In this it takes as its technical model the " statue," where the raw material of bronze receives some definite shape or form. *Hylosystemism*, on the other hand, explains the constitution of the natural body as an *atomary energy system*, in the sense that the atom of an element and the molecule of a compound are composed of sub-atomic particles (protons, electrons, etc.) united into a *dynamic system* working as a *functional unit*.[2]

In other words these philosophers are implicitly following the 'realist' school, and are hypostatising the picture of the nature of matter put forward by the modern physicist.

Bittle goes on[3] :

It is not the technical hylomorphic model of the 'statue' with its intimately united matter and shape which fits the facts of physics and chemistry, but the technical hylomeric model of a 'house' as a system composed of many heterogeneous materials. One set

----

[1] Except for the underlying modifications necessitated in recent years by the theory of wave mechanics.

[2] *Ibid.* p. 322.

[3] *Ibid.* p. 332.

of materials can be replaced by another; the materials may be removed, exchanged, or re-arranged, so that the result will be a different type of house.

Hylosystemism, it is claimed, gives a more rational explanation of the facts of change in inorganic bodies than does hylomorphism. Modern science, it is held, has rendered hylomorphism inadequate, while favouring hylosystemism.

When substantial change occurs, according to Aristotle and St. Thomas, the body retains its primary matter, but loses its old form and takes on a new one. Hylosystemists, on the other hand, virtually deny that there are any real substantial changes. What appears to be a substantial change in nature consists in reality, they say, of a regrouping of the atomic and subatomic parts. There are many arguments *pro* and *con* the two theories which will be found set out by Bittle.

There has been a tendency among some hylomorphists in recent times to steer a middle course and to modify the traditional hylomorphism of Aristotle and St. Thomas in a direction which, they think, makes it more amenable to modern science, without abandoning the principle. The traditional theory applied hylomorphism to the ordinary natural bodies in the world about us. Some philosophers in modern times, however, accepting the atomic theory, have ascribed separate forms to each atom. Since the atom has now been resolved into a complex dynamical system, philosophers pursuing this line have been obliged to give separate substantial forms to the individual sub-atomic particles. This means that ordinary material bodies are merely aggregates. Changes, then, are accidental, not substantial. This, as Bittle points out, is *reductio ad absurdum* of traditional hylomorphism as it denies the starting point of the whole system, namely, that substantial changes occur in the world about us. *It is clear that any modification of hylomorphism in the direction of atomism leads to its ultimate destruction.*

Hylosystemism, too, of course, makes changes accidental and not substantial ; but in this it is not denying its own foundations, as is modified hylomorphism.

To the criticism that hylosystemism is merely hypostatising the latest scientific theory of the nature of physical bodies, and is building its house on the ever-shifting sands of these scientific theories, Bittle makes the specious rejoinder that the hylomorphism of Aristotle, too, was founded on the latest scientific theories of his day. This rejoinder is specious because the doctrine of Aristotle and St. Thomas was not founded on any *particular* facts at all. It was founded on observations of such a general and universal nature : that bodies exist and that they obviously undergo substantial change, that no subsequent discoveries could possibly affect the truth of this basic contention. We may compare this with the starting point for one of the Thomistic arguments for the existence of God, namely : that something exists. This proposition is of such a universal nature that no special facts could possibly invalidate it. Hence this argument for God's existence is founded on solid rock, so to speak, and the storms of time can never overthrow it.

This distinction between the shifting sands of passing theories and particular 'facts,' and the absolute assurance of universal observations, is something which Bittle appears to overlook in comparing hylosystemism and hylomorphism.

As Bittle himself admits,[1] the incoming of the most recent theory, that of wave mechanics, propounded some twenty years ago by Heisenberg and Schrödinger, which we have previously mentioned,[2] is already endangering hylosystemism, since it is a return to a modified theory of the *continuity* of matter, as distinct from a system of discrete particles on which hylosystemism is founded.

It is not difficult to see why some modern Scholastic philosophers have advanced modified-hylomorphism, and hylosystemism. It is because they have taken the theories of modern physics very seriously. They have forgotten the wise injunction of Cardinal Bellarmine,[3] and have ascribed a

---

[1] *Ibid.* pp. 338–339.
[2] p. 63.
[3] pp. 198-9.

real ontological status to the picture of the nature of the physical world advanced by the modern physicist.

But, of course, if the theory of modern physics advanced in this work, with its distinction of *nomos* and *physis*, is well founded, then the atoms and the 'hylons' are not to be regarded as real, but as more in the nature of mnemonics or mental artifices devised for a utilitarian end. There is no need to repeat here the discussion of previous chapters. It will be clear to the reader that there is no call on the philosopher to attempt to keep pace with modern physics. And, indeed, such an attempt would be as futile as it is misguided, since physics is ever changing.

*The general conclusion, then, is that the traditional doctrine of hylomorphism of Aristotle and St. Thomas is unshaken.*

Modern Scholastic philosophers who have attempted to modify it have done it a disservice. In its modified atomic form it is eventually reduced to absurdity. Hylosystemism is a new approach, but it has only a weak foundation on *particular* 'facts' in ever-changing theories.

Only the traditional hylomorphism is based on universality and is therefore enduring.

## Professor Whittaker

Professor Whittaker, the eminent mathematical physicist, is a Scholastic unifier who approaches the subject from a direction diametrically opposite to that of hylosystemism.

In an interesting and thoughtful article published recently, Professor Whittaker has surveyed the progress of modern physics from its inception in the 17th century until the present day.[1] His contention is that after the violent reaction from Aristoteleanism in the 17th century, physics has gradually been moving back more and more into conformity with the Aristotelean world picture.

Absolute space and time were basic in the Newtonian scheme.

---

[1] Whittaker : *Phil. Mag.*, xxxiv, 266, 1943, ' *Aristotle, Newton, Einstein.*' (Address of the President at the Annual Statutory Meeting of the Royal Society of Edinburgh, Oct. 26, 1942).

The physical world was described in terms of material bodies persisting in time and moving in space under the influence of force.

But, with the progress of time, attention was given more and more to minimum principles and less and less to mechanical forces. This culminated in 1916 in Einstein's General Theory of Relativity. Whittaker writes[1] :

In Einstein's theory of gravitation the Newtonian concept of force is completely done away with ; a free particle moves in a path determined solely by the curvature-properties of space ; it is, as the Aristoteleans would say, *in potency* with regard to space, and things in a state of potency continually seek to become actualized. The changes of position of the particle in their turn bring about changes in the curvature of space, so that the particle and space together may be regarded as a single system whose evolution is determined by the law that the total curvature of space-time is to be a minimum : as we may say, *gravitation represents a continual effort of the universe to straighten itself out*—a statement so completely teleological that it would certainly have delighted the hearts of Schoolmen.[2]

Another avenue in which Professor Whittaker sees growing conformity with the Scholastic principles is in the quantum theory and the structure of the atom. He draws attention to Bohr's theory of stationary states of the atom and the absence from the theory of a precise explanation of the transition of the atom from one state to the other. Space and time thus lose the dominant position which they held in Newtonianism. They are relegated to a lower status resembling that which they held in Scholasticism, where space is but one among the ten Predicaments or Categories of Being. In this new scheme :

[1] *Ibid.* p. 275.

[2] Note : That this is the significance of the Einstein theory of gravitation is certainly far from what its propounder envisaged. Einstein, following Ernst Mach, was spurred towards a general theory of relativity, which would deal with rotation as well as translation, by the desire to preserve a purely empirical and phenomenalistic theory of knowledge. This is a far cry from teleology. See § 2 of Einstein's article ' *Die Grundlage der allgemeinen Relativitätstheorie* ' : *Annalen der Physik*, 49, 769, 1916. English translation in : Einstein and Others : *The Principle of Relativity* (London). Einstein here lays down that ' No answer can be admitted as epistemologically satisfactory unless the reason given is an observable fact of experience.'

' The atom, which has a potency of various states, is correlated to the states, as potency is to act. It endures as the atom, while it takes different states in succession. This is precisely the aspect of things on which Aristotle fixed his attention : that substratum which persists while receiving different determinations is what in the Aristotelean-Scholastic philosophy is called *matter* ; whereas the structural principle, which is peculiar to each determination or state, is called *form*. The atom, then, is *matter* with respect to its states, which are *forms*.'[1]

Whittaker goes on to apply similar considerations to the present-day theory of the nucleus as composed of protons and neutrons. The proton and the neutron may be regarded as two states of a single entity, i.e. matter and two possible forms.

Whittaker comes finally to a rather surprising conclusion[2]

' It therefore becomes necessary to find a metaphysics different from that which has been associated with classical physics ; for metaphysics must (as Aristotle held) originate with reference to physics, since it is the conceptual framework into which our experience of Nature is to be fitted. The progress of science has destroyed the foundations on which natural philosophy has hitherto been grounded.'

If Whittaker means, as he appears to do, that metaphysics is the conceptual framework into which our experience of Nature is to be fitted, then it is difficult to see how any system of physics can affect metaphysics, since any such system will be built up in the given metaphysical framework. Consequently it is not clear how changes in physics have made it necessary to find a new metaphysics, unless we take a very pragmatic view of metaphysics, which is certainly not the Scholastic view.

The fact is, as we have stressed already in discussing hylo-systemism, that Scholastic metaphysics is independent of any *particular* theory of physics, being grounded on principles so general that no changes in the theories of physics can affect them. This feature of Scholastic metaphysics Whittaker appears to have overlooked.

[1] *Ibid.* p. 277.
[2] *Ibid.* p. 277.

Whittaker, too, has not considered the Procrustean theory of modern 'physics.' He has not distinguished between *physis* and *nomos*. Had he done so he would not have reached the conclusion that the changes in modern 'physics' point to any particular theory of metaphysics. Considered as *nomos*, the modern 'physicist' can propound any theory which pragmatic success dictates. Such theories may or may not have resemblances to teleology or hylomorphism. Any such resemblances, or lack of them, will be purely accidental and of no philosophical import at all.

It may be, as Whittaker maintains, that some theories of modern physics can be given something of a 'Scholastic' colouring. But modern physics, exercising its autonomy, may in years to come present quite a different picture. Then to follow Whittaker's line of argument we should have to abandon Scholastic metaphysics. To found metaphysics on the latest theories of Procrustean physics is very precarious, as well as being philosophically unsound.

Hylosystemism favours recasting Scholastic metaphysics, or some of it, to bring it into conformity with modern physics. Professor Whittaker on the other hand believes that modern physics itself is moving towards conformity with Scholastic metaphysics. Coming as they do from opposite directions, both schools of thought cannot be right. In fact it is our contention that neither school is right. They both hypostatise modern physical theories, and they both lose sight of the fact that Scholastic metaphysics is not founded on any *particular* theory of physics at all.

Let us now turn to a point of view which offers much more promise of arriving at a satisfactory solution—that of the dualists.

# CHAPTER XX

## THE SCHOLASTIC DUALISTS

BELLARMINE divined, albeit dimly, that there are two orders, but gave no adequate account of how they came to be. The principal activity of modern Scholastics in this field is to attempt to supply the missing account. There are various theories on the subject.

### Duhem and Maritain

Some philosophers have fallen back on the rather evasive phrase 'primary and secondary causes.' Metaphysics deals with primary causes, physical science with secondary causes. But this theory is hardly satisfactory. For one thing it is so vague and general that it really explains nothing. Furthermore it seems natural to suppose that we could trace back through secondary causes to primary causes, so there are not really two divisions or orders at all, but only one. This, then, does not account adequately for the autonomy of empirical science.

Other philosophers have drawn attention, more cogently, to the old distinction of how and why. Science tells us *how* things happen, philosophy *why* they happen. Such a distinction is to be found in St. Thomas.[1] On the one hand we have empirical statements, on the other explanation. This theme is developed in recent times by such writers as Pierre Duhem[2] and later Jacques Maritain,[3] under the stimulus of the phenomenalist school of physical thought, which accords well with the how-why distinction. Physical science, dealing with

---

[1] See Phillips, R. P. : *Modern Thomistic Philosophy*, v. 2, p. 153.
[2] See, amongst other works, his *La Théorie Physique*.
[3] Maritain, J. : *The Degrees of Knowledge* (Eng. Tr.), Ch. I, § 3, etc. Maritain's theories are a development of Duhem's. We shall only discuss Maritain here.

phenomena, tells us *how* things happen.   Philosophy's task is
to tell us *why* they happen.

In one passage Maritain writes :

In my opinion it is necessary to abandon, as contrary to the
nature of things, the hope of finding any continuity or close connection in regard to the explication of the real, I do not say in
regard to the *facts* (in so far as they can be isolated from theory),
but the *theories*, the conceptual elaborations of mathematical
physics, and the proper texture of philosophical and metaphyiscal
knowledge.   The discontinuity is very clear cut and is due to the
very essence of these sciences.   Mathematical physics is not a
formally physical science :  if it is directly physical in regard to the
matter whereby it verifies its judgments, if it is orientated towards
an end in the physically real and physical causes, it is not in order
to grasp their intimate ontological nature.[1]

In other words he distinguishes as it were two orders—the
physical and the ontological.   He proceeds to elaborate the
character of the physical order :  that it is partial and has as
its aim the attainment of a coherent system.

He writes :

Physics . . . only envisages this ontological reality, these
physical causes, from the angle of mathematics ;  it only considers
them in pursuit of certain analytic translations, in divisions effected
by mathematical means.   It retains of the real only its measurable
bearing, the measurements taken of it by our instruments—and it
is thanks to these measurements, which are certainly real, that the
entities and symbols of mathematical physics have a foundation in
reality.   But it is in the measurable that it resolves all its concepts,
which alone has a meaning for it.   And once in possession of its
measurements it essentially lives by weaving between them a web
of mathematical relations deductive in form, which constitute its
formal object and which doubtless need to be completed by a
certain hypothetical reconstruction of the physically real, but from
which it is only asked that their ultimate numerical result should
coincide with the measurements of things effected by our instruments
. . . A physico-mathematical theory is called 'true' when the
coherent system and the fullest possible range of mathematical
symbols and explicatory entities which it is able to organise coincides

[1] *Ibid.* p. 76.

in all its numerical conclusions with the real measurements effected by us, without it being in the least necessary that any physical reality, a certain nature or ontological law in the world of bodies, should *precisely* correspond with each of the symbols and mathematical entities which are in question.

Maritain makes his attitude somewhat more precise by invoking the doctrine of the *ens rationis*,[1] a doctrine to which we have already drawn attention.[2]  He writes :

because rational being constitutes the specific object of logic (that is the privilege of that science) we are tempted to believe that these *entia rationis* only play a part in logic :  a grave error indeed.[3]

He contends that a great number of rational beings are used in modern physics as auxiliaries.   This science does not pursue causes and essences in themselves, but instead reconstructs with rational beings a physical system embodying the relations of measurement with which it is concerned.   It was in this way that physics gained its autonomy from philosophy.   Other sciences have followed its example in varying degrees.

He sums up :

It is not *what things are in themselves* which is the point of interest ; what is important are the possibilities of empiric proof and of mensuration which they represent, and also of connecting together, according to certain stable laws, the data furnished by these means. Every definition must be made, no longer 'by the nearest gender and specific difference,' but by observable and highly determined measurable properties, to each of which is assigned in each case the method of recording and of practical verification.

The possibility of observation and measurement thus replaces for such forms of knowledge the essence or quiddity sought for in things by philosophy.[4]

Physics, then, lives by weaving between its measurements a web of mathematical relations, and thereby elaborates a hypothetical construction. This construction does not precisely correspond with the real.

Finally :

There is perhaps an element of melancholy in this assertion

---

[1] *Ibid.* Ch. III.
[2] See pp. 188 f.
[3] *Ibid.* p. 170.
[4] *Ibid.* p. 182.

that the image of the universe, or more exactly the more or less discordant images and shadow-images in which it appears in the last analysis the explicatory effort of physical theories can only result, cannot be, as was for so long believed, the natural prolongation of the ontological explications supplied by philosophy.[1]

Later in this work[2] he compares scientific imagery to myths. And, as he points out,[3] the central fault of modern philosophy in the sphere of natural knowledge has been to give an ontological value to such myths.

Maritain's separation into two orders, and his account of the scientific order as building up myths out of *entia rationis* to give the most coherent account of the phenomena, is excellent as far as it goes.   But it is still vague and incomplete.   He says that the scientific construction need not *precisely* correspond with the real.   But he does not make the degree of correspondence clear, nor does he explain how the transition to *entia rationis* is effected.   We have, indeed, the general principle plainly enough, but the burning question of what *precisely* is the relation between the orders, and *how* the physical order is generated, still eludes us.

Although the general how-why distinction is still vague and elusive, yet it has the undoubted merit of drawing forcible attention to a fundamental point :  the *partial* nature of modern science.

Probably the most common practice amongst Scholastic cosmologists today is simply to assert that there *is* a scientific order, and there *is* a philosophical order, and leave it at that. Thus a recent writer, J. J. Colligan, in his *Cosmology : A Philosophical Study of the Corporeal World*, distinguishes between scientific atomism and philosophical atomism.[4]  He refutes the latter on philosophical grounds, but is careful to point out that this does not apply to :

any theory which is purely scientific and which, therefore, pertains

---

[1] *Ibid.* p. 80.
[2] *Ibid.* p. 223.
[3] *Ibid.* p. 225.
[4] cf. the distinction we drew in Ch. V between empirical atomism and metaphysical atomism.

to the experimental sciences, and is demonstrable by experiment or observation in the scientific laboratory.[1]

He goes on:

Scholastic philosophy finds nothing in the theory of Scientific Atomism which cannot harmonize with its principles. The theory is physical in the sense that it deals with empirical investigation. It is, therefore, not metaphysical and is outside our field of investigation.[2]

These sentiments are admirable, but they are not one step in advance of the suggestion of Cardinal Bellarmine, made centuries ago. The student still wants to know precisely how and why the two orders are independent, and what relation, if any, subsists between them.

## O'Rahilly

Mention must be made of the pertinent doctrines contained in a recent work by Professor Alfred O'Rahilly,[3] who writes with a Scholastic background. This comprehensive and provocative work is permeated through and through with the dichotomy of the two orders. O'Rahilly defends the general phenomenalist theory of modern physics, upholds the philosophical neutrality and pragmatic character of physics, and belabours the physicists who erect their physical theories into ontological realities and argue about the constitution of the world. Disputes in physics, he says, 'provide an opportunity for examining our equations, not our consciences.'[4] He distinguishes carefully between the discourse of the physicists and the quantitative formulation of physics.[5] The latter, founded on empirical verification at every step, is the sole relevant ground for scientific argument. Discussions about the former are scientifically merely sterile. What pertains to the discourse is:

often a farrago of philosophy, paradox and imagination, in which physicists so often indulge when writing semi-philosophical or

[1] p. 74.
[2] p. 76.
[3] *Electromagnetics : A Discussion of Fundamentals* (1938).
[4] *Ibid.* p. 628.
[5] *Ibid.* p. 637.

popular books and even when writing text books. The question
to be asked concerning any hypothesis is this: Does it in any way
influence the measure numbers which are to be tested by the man
in the laboratory? If it does not, it may be good or bad philosophy;
but it is not physics.[1]

Discourse on lines of force, ether, fields, etc., may be
provided as a pedagogical concession to human weakness in
grasping physics. But they are not to be believed in, only
to be used.[2]

Again O'Rahilly writes:

We must learn the laws and properties . . . before we start
enquiring into causes; we can find these laws though the causes
be not yet discovered. This would be a great step in physics which
is a practical affair comparable to the art of a clockmaker.[3]

### *Incompleteness of These Doctrines : The Root*

While we may heartily concur in general with Professor
O'Rahilly's views about physics, yet there is still something
missing. His is another version of the 'how' and 'why'
distinction. 'We must learn the laws and properties before
we start enquiring into the causes' he tells us, yet we cannot
but feel that *real* laws and properties could not be so clearly
divorced from causes.

Phillips, in discussing 'phenomenalism' versus 'realism'
in physics, remarks aptly in this connection:

The other extreme (phenomenalism) seems also to be inadmissible, inasmuch as the theories are founded on quantitative
examination of the material world, and therefore cannot be wholly
unconnected with the material reality of which it is composed.
From this it is clear that philosophy cannot ignore physical theory,
nor yet regard it as expressed in the same language as that which
it uses itself.[4]

These various upholders of the dualist theory have based
themselves on *passive* phenomenalism. The difficulties which
they encounter, and the vague state in which they are obliged
to leave the subject, all arise from the character of this basis.

---

[1] *Ibid.* p. 637.
[2] This of course is just Mach's doctrine of 'mental artifices' (p. 206.)
[3] *Ibid.* p. 641.
[4] *Modern Thomistic Philosophy, v.* 1, p. 165.

But if, instead of *passive* phenomenalism, we base our theory on the *active* Procrustean phenomenalism expounded in this work,[1] the difficulties vanish. For with active phenomenalism we sever the *immediate* link between the phenomena and the real ontological ground. This gives physical science its complete autonomy, and so provides us with the two separate and independent orders so long sought for by the dualist philosophers.

[1] See particularly Ch. XVIII.

# CHAPTER XXI

# THE END OF THE ROAD

THE solution to the problem is now before us. The quest of the modern cosmologist for a satisfactory harmony of Thomism with post-Galilean physical science is nearing its goal.

The bifurcation made by the Procrustean interpretation of physics rescues the dualist theory from the *impasse* in which it has been struggling. With our discussion of voluntary active phenomenalism in Ch. XVIII in view, we can see precisely how there come to be two orders, each autonomous. The Scholastic metaphysician functions in one order, the modern physicist in the other, and there is no immediate link whatever between them. There is a clean divorce between the ontological reality, and the physical laws and properties which belong to the categorial order.

The link between the physical laws and the underlying causes is no longer of the first remove but of the second. The fundamental dictum of Wittgenstein is our guide here[1] : that a law of physics applies tells us nothing about the world, but only that it applies in the way in which in fact it does apply, tells us something about the world.

This all-important consequence of the Procrustean character of modern physics provides the solution to Phillips' difficulty.[2] It furnishes the essential supplement to the otherwise admirable doctrines of O'Rahilly and Maritain.

This doctrine of the two orders, soundly based, is very much more satisfactory than such a palliative as hylosystemism.

---

[1] See p. 98.
[2] See p. 224. The difficulty of course arises from the failure to distinguish the physicists' data from phenomena. We are careful to distinguish them.

Now we can retain the Thomist doctrine in all its purity, but we have added to it another chapter, so that the post-Renaissance physical science may at last find a home in the ample structure of the *philosophia perennis*.

It is from Immanuel Kant that this doctrine of the nature of modern physics ultimately derives. Scholastics thus owe to Kant the recognition that he, albeit unwittingly, has made one of the greatest contributions to the *philosophia perennis* since St. Thomas.

It is commonly stated that St. Thomas showed that there is no contradiction between faith and profane science. This is true of sciences of the real. But for sciences of the categorial we must look also to Kant. It is St. Thomas and Kant between them who have shown that there is no contradiction possible between faith and *any* profane science.

Let us now summarise the contents of these chapters.

The Bellarmine dichotomy between what actually is the case, and what gives the most satisfactory empirical explanation, has all along been the basic contention of the dualist philosophers. But the absence hitherto of an adequate explanation of how there can be these two separate orders has been the great stumbling block. It has driven other Scholastic philosophers virtually to abandon the dichotomy and try to work out a unitary theory. This has led to such a scheme as hylosystemism with its fundamental distortions of Thomism.

We have shown how illusory such unitary schemes must be, founded as they are on the shifting sands of current physical theories.

On the other hand we have supplied the missing explanation in the dualist theory. By pointing out the Procrustean categorial nature of modern physics, we have established its autonomy on a satisfactory basis. We have shown how the two orders can exist side by side without clashing. Hence the Thomist structure needs no alterations, but only the extension of a wing to the house.

We have traced in outline the slow recognition by Scholastic philosophers of the part played by artifacts, or *entia rationis*, call them what we will, in the new physical learning which has been developing since the 17th century.

The time has now come for this recognition to be extended to a wider field than merely that of modern physics.   We have seen in this work how systems of artifacts are to be found in a great variety of human pursuits.   In nearly all our activities we avail ourselves of their assistance ; we find at almost every turn a fabric woven of myths.   Such a fabric is necessary to facilitate our passage through the world.   But we must never lose sight of the fact that it *is* only myths and phantoms.   We should never allow ourselves to be enslaved by our own creations : there are no bonds more insidious than those we impose on ourselves.

Behind the shadowy world we have created to be our servant, there lies the real world.   A phantom is but a sorry companion to any man.   It is the real world, the world which ever is, to which we must turn our eyes, and from which comes our strength.

# PRE-GALILEAN PHYSICAL PHILOSOPHY

In this work we have been principally concerned with an examination of the nature of various modern sciences, particularly of physical science. We have traced back the development of physical science to the days of Galileo, and have contrasted the nature of post-Galilean science with pre-Galilean science.

So as to simplify the discussion, and bring out the distinction of the real and the categorial with the maximum clarity, we have so far given no more than cursory attention to the theories and controversies of the days before Galileo.

While it is sufficient as a first approximation to take Galileo as the great divide between the old and the new, between a world pre-occupied with the *physis* on the one hand, and a world pre-occupied with the *nomos* on the other, yet it must be remembered that this *is* only a first approximation. A more detailed examination of the situation shows that the actual course of history is much more complex than our simplified representation. The movements are, in reality, not nearly so clear-cut and separate ; instead they interpenetrate in a network of cross-strands.

Indeed, we find in history in general, that history as it is popularly written is much over-simplified. Terms like 'The Renaissance' and 'The Industrial Revolution' cannot be taken too much *au pied de la lettre*. Taken as indicating broad divisions they are useful in organizing the subject (organizing it in fact in a 'categorial' scheme) ; taken as anything more, they are only a source of obscurity.

The history of physical science is no exception to this general rule. When we examine the matter more closely we find the threads stretching back far behind Galileo. Pre-Galilean notions of physical theory are as varied and penetrating, if more circumscribed, than those of later days. Indeed this field is comparable to the field of pre-Socratic philosophy, or of theories of evolution before Darwin.

Unfortunately, as yet, the authors of the 14th, 15th and 16th centuries have been little studied. Most of their works are difficult of access, and in fact not a few of the earlier works have never been printed and are still in manuscript form. The labours of the great French physicist, historian, and philosopher, Pierre Duhem, nearly half a century ago, provided us with a veritable mine of information. His is an invaluable reconnaissance. Since then sporadic attention has been paid to the period, and a few texts have been edited. But most historians, alas, still dismiss the period with some vague reference to the 'decadent' Scholastics, in the naïve belief that after the great philosophical heights reached in the 13th century, the ensuing centuries were ones of slow decay and degeneration.

Little though there is yet accessible of the later Scholasticism, what glimpses we have suggest a rich and fertile terrain. Not only can we trace back, for centuries behind the 17th, many of the distinctive physical ideas of Galileo, such as the non-differentiation of terrestrial and celestial realms, the principle of inertia, the equal acceleration of all falling bodies, and so on ; not only this, which is here perhaps of somewhat academic interest, but we also find in those earlier centuries the most acute discussions of the ontological status of the hypothetical elements of a science, and clear enunciations of the principle of two orders in physics, or more specifically, in astronomy : the real order on the one hand, and on the other the fictional order, or as we have called it, the order of 'artifacts.'

These latter discussions of the nature of physical and more particularly astronomical theories, were completely forgotten in the later times. The 17th, 18th and 19th centuries were oblivious to them. Theories advanced in modern times, e.g. Ernst Mach's,[1] regarded as very daring and epoch-making,

[1] p. 206.

are to be found in substance in the forefront of many of the writings of the later Middle Ages. Some of these later Scholastics handle the theme with a brilliance and penetration scarcely to be matched in our own day.

Pre-Galilean physical philosophy merits extensive treatment. But we will have space here for only the briefest *résumé*. It will be based on the investigations of Pierre Duhem published in 1908 as an Essay under the title of '*Saving the Appearances.*' Recourse should be had to these papers for details, and in particular for references to the original writings on the basis of which Duhem composed his history of the philosophy of physical theory.[1]

In such an historical discussion it must be borne in mind that before the 17th century there was scarcely any exact science corresponding to our modern mathematical physics. In its place was the exact science of astronomy. The problem confronting the learned world, from the Greeks to the time of the Renaissance, was not the status of what we would now call physical theory, but the analogous problem of the status of astronomical theory. Our question: what is the relation of physical theory to metaphysics? was, before the 17th century, the question: what is the relation of astronomical theory to the real constitution of the world?

We may have rational grounds for believing that the real constitution of the world is of such and such a nature. On the other hand the practical astronomer who is concerned primarily with accounting for the observations, with 'saving the appearances,' may develop a different system of his own. How is the mathematical system of the observational astronomer related to the real nature of things?

That there will be two lines of development, the one integrated with metaphysics, and the other more remote, seems to be envisaged by Aristotle. In the *Physics* (193[b]) Aristotle writes:

[1] Duhem, Pierre : *Essai sur la notion de Théorie physique de Platon à Galilée* : *Annales de philosophie chrétienne*, Sept. 1908. This Essay was reprinted under the Greek title ΣΩΖΕΙΝ ΤΑ ΦΑΙΝΟΜΕΝΑ. Unfortunately, this work is not readily accessible in the English-speaking world. The original articles may be consulted, however, in such libraries as that of the British Museum.

Further, is astronomy different from physics or a department of it ?  It seems absurd that the physicist should be supposed to know the nature of sun or moon, but not to know any of their essential attributes, particularly as the writers on physics obviously do discuss their shape also and whether the earth and the world are spherical or not.

Now the mathematician, though he; too, treats of these things, nevertheless does not treat of them as the limits of a physical body ; nor does he consider the attributes indicated as the attributes of such bodies.

There we have the basis of a cleavage between physics and metaphysics on the one hand, and mathematical astronomy on the other.  With the development of astronomy this cleavage was to become greater and greater.

On quasi-metaphysical grounds Aristotle held that the Universe is spherical and that the celestial orbs revolve with a uniform circular motion about the centre of the World, this centre being occupied by the stationary Earth.

However, as observational astronomy developed, the mathematical astronomers increasingly abandoned Aristotle's simple combination of concentric spheres, and substituted for it an ever more elaborate system of cycles, epicycles, and eccentrics, in the heavens.  This system reached its highest perfection in the ancient world in the system of Ptolemy propounded in the 2nd century A.D. in the great work which the Arabs called *Almagest*.

The orthodox peripatetics were obliged to reject this elaborate system as metaphysically impossible, and yet it cannot be denied that it, and it alone, saves the appearances ;  the Aristotelean system of concentric spheres, while conforming to metaphysical requirements, is not able to account for all the observed movements of the heavenly bodies.

What are we to make of these two schools of thought ? Some Greek philosophers insisted on the mathematician conforming to metaphysics; they would not allow the astronomer his autonomy ;  for an astronomer to use a metaphysically impossible system was absurd, they believed, however successful the system may appear to be in accounting for the heavenly movements. Nevertheless, if a system were successful in practice it could scarcely be ignored, whatever weighty objections the metaphysicians might raise.

At the other extreme, some held that the mathematical systems must occupy first place; that they alone informed us of the true nature of the world, and that if metaphysics conflicted with them then so much the worse for metaphysics; that to account for the observations is the touch-stone of truth. This intransigeant attitude was considerably embarrassed, however, by the reflection that there were various alternative mathematical systems which equally accounted for the observations; the simple hypostatising of some system was then scarcely possible, since there can be only one nature of things.

In the terminology we have hitherto employed, it will be apparent that both these schools of thought subscribed to the realist principle of *one order*; but that they each approached this single order from diametrically opposed sides.

The more mature thought of the Greek world, however, followed up Aristotle's hint, and developed the idea of *two orders*, each independent of the other. This receives its clearest expression in the writings of the neo-Platonist philosopher Simplicius (*fl.* 6th century A.D.) who, to quote Duhem, 'gives the most exact account of the rôle of astronomer and physicist to be found in antiquity.' Simplicius, quoting earlier authors, writes[1]:

It pertains to physical theory to examine what concerns the essence of the sky and the stars, their power, their quality, their generation and destruction; and by Jupiter, it must also be able to give demonstrations concerning the magnitude, the figure, and the order, of these bodies. Astronomy, on the contrary, has no aptitude to speak of these first things; but its demonstrations have for their object the order of the celestial bodies, after it has declared that the sky is truly ordered; it discourses on the figures, the size, and distances of the Earth, of the Sun, and of the Moon; it speaks of eclipses, of the conjunctions of the stars, of the qualitative and quantitative properties of their movements. Since then it depends

[1] Duhem, pp. 121 f.

on the theory which considers the figures from the point of view of quality, size, and quantity, it is fitting that it requires the aid of Arithmetic and Geometry. . . . Very often, moreover, Astronomy and Physics take the same chapter of the Science as the object of their demonstrations; they propose, e.g., to prove that the Sun is great, or that the Earth is spherical; but in this case they do not proceed by the same road; *the physicist must demonstrate each of his propositions by drawing them from the essence of the bodies, from their powers, from what best suits their perfection, from their generation, from their transformation; the Astronomer on the contrary establishes them by means of the circumstances which accompany the sizes and shapes, from the qualitative particulars of the movement, from the times corresponding to this movement.* . . .

This doctrine expounded by Simplicius represents the high water mark of Greek philosophy in our subject. It allows the astronomer to free himself from the physicist or metaphysician, and to employ his own methods in order to 'save the appearances.' On the other hand it does not subject the metaphysician to the dictates of the astronomer since the entities of the astronomer are fictions and artifices. Such was the balanced and harmonious teaching which the Greek world handed down to later ages. Sometimes it was heeded, sometimes it was not.

Before leaving the ancient world we must notice yet another doctrine on the subject; it is an example of 'coming events casting their shadows before,' since its principles have assumed vast proportions in modern times. This is the sceptical or positivist doctrine propounded for instance by the neo-Platonist Proclus of Byzantium who flourished in the 5th century A.D. Proclus held that the hypothetical eccentrics, epicycles, and so on, of the astronomers, are pure abstractions; furthermore, *God alone* knows the exact constitution of the heavens, man can have only a fictional knowledge of it; we can know nothing of the essences in the celestial realms. From the celestial metaphysics of Aristotle the wheel has indeed gone full circle. Nevertheless, Duhem points out, this positivism is confined to celestial matters; for Proclus, we can still know the natures in the sub-lunary world, i.e. we can have a real terrestrial physics.   Only in the later Middle Ages, when the distinction between celestial and sub-lunary bodies slowly disappeared, do we find these celestial principles of Proclus being made general, and so leading into modern positivism.

Thus we see that although its attention was confined to the one exact science of Astronomy, the Greek world gave us the first formulations of the doctrines of the Unifiers, of the Dualists, and of the simple phenomenalists.   Of these schools of thought, that of the Dualists is undoubtedly the most rational.

The subsequent history of the philosophy of astronomical theories is largely one of cycles.   At some periods there was little or no discussion of fundamentals.   At other periods interest was keen and the arguments of the various Greek schools were taken up anew in various ways.

During the earlier Middle Ages, Duhem finds little critical discussion of the nature of astronomical hypotheses.   Philosophy in this field slept, and practice reigned supreme.   But there was a gradual re-awakening of consciousness, and by the 12th century mature philosophies were again being propounded.

The great Jewish philosopher of Cordoba, Moses Maimonides (1135–1204), held views on astronomy similar to those of Proclus.   For him the knowledge of the real nature of the celestial world surpasses the powers of man.   'What Aristotle says concerning things above the sphere of the moon is, with few exceptions, mere imagination and opinion' writes Maimonides in his *Guide for the Perplexed*.[1]   'Of the things in the heavens man knows nothing except a few mathematical calculations, and you see how far these go.   I say in the words of the poet " The heavens are the Lord's, but the earth He hath given to the sons of man " (*Psalm* cxv, 16), that is to say, God alone has a perfect and true knowledge of the heavens, their nature, their essence, their form, their motions, and their causes.'[2]   While we cannot have knowledge of the

---

[1] *Guide for the Perplexed* (tr. M. Friedlander (London, 1881-85)), Part II, Ch. XXII.
[2] *Ibid.* Ch. XXIV.

essence of the heavens, yet we can still have a mathematical astronomy, for the object of the astronomer is not to know the real nature of the heavens, but 'simply to find an hypothesis that would lead to a uniform and circular motion of the stars without acceleration, retardation, or change, and which is in its effects in accordance with observation. He will, besides, endeavour to find such an hypothesis which would require the least complicated motion.'[1]

The contemporary Arabic philosophers were not astronomical positivists, like Maimonides, but were, on the contrary, intransigeant realists. They combined this astronomical realism with a fervent adherence to the peripatetic philosophy of Aristotle. This involved a complete rejection of the doctrines of the *Almagest*, for Ptolemy had invoked eccentrics and epicycles, and these are quite inadmissible on the peripatetic physics. The greatest of the Arabians was Averroes (1126–1198), like Maimonides, a native of Cordoba. Averroes, unlike Maimonides, will not allow astronomers the right to use their own hypotheses in order to save the appearances. He has some very pertinent criticism of the Ptolemaic methods, from the point of view of the realist. (It is quoted by Duhem). For Averroes, Astronomy in his time did not really exist; he determined therefore to construct a true Astronomy on the basis of the real nature of things as known in Physics and Metaphysics, a true Astronomy which would also save the appearances. His disciple, Al Bitrogi, worked out the details of this system. The concentric sphere system of Al Bitrogi was defended up to the 17th century by the Averroists. The Al Bitrogi *v*. Ptolemy debate persisted until the system of Copernicus came to challenge them both. The parties to this old dispute were both realists. Had they reflected on the theory of two orders, one real, the other fictional, by means of which the two requirements of reason and prediction had been reconciled in the Greek world, this controversy could have been settled amicably.

St. Thomas Aquinas (1225–1274) revived this principle

[1] *Ibid.* Ch. XI.

of two orders in his Exposition on Aristotle's *De Caelo et Mundo*. We have already alluded to this in Ch. XVII. Metaphysically it seems that we can admit only of uniform rotations about the centre of the Universe; on the other hand to agree with our observations we need the eccentrics and epicycles of Ptolemy. We can admit these latter as devices to account for the movements. In fact many such devices can be worked out. But we must not give them any real status ; they are convenient fictions and nothing more.

Following thus in the path of Simplicius, St. Thomas reconciles the aims of the physicist and the aims of the practical astronomer by the notion of two orders.

After the keen philosophical consciousness of the 12th and 13th centuries, when we come to the 14th century we find in our field a period of quiescence, so far as the researches of Duhem reveal. It was another interlude during which there was little criticism of the fundamentals of mathematical science.

However, the forces were gathering for a new period of intense criticism. Towards the end of the 15th century we hear its rumblings.

At this time the different Universities tended to profess different astronomical loyalties. The University of Vienna, for instance, was Ptolemaic; they accepted the principles of the system of the *Almagest* as established for ever, and set themselves the task of perfecting its details. On the other hand the University of Padua, was, for the most part, staunchly Averroist. These Averroists denied the right of astronomers to use hypotheses not in conformity with the peripatetic physics; consequently they rejected the *Almagest*, and adhered to a system of concentric spheres. Tension must have been high at Padua, for there were also Ptolemaians in the University. These Ptolemaians were as firm realists as were the Averroists.

Cutting across both these opposing realist schools came the Humanists; they were a powerful party at Paris from the end of the 15th century. In Astronomy the Humanists were inclined to scepticism and fell into line with Proclus and

Maimonides. Astronomy for them became a sort of geometrical recipe-book for constructing tables to forecast celestial movements.

One of their leaders at Paris was Lefèvre d'Étaples; for him Astronomy was an affair of representation and imagination. In this, he was a true disciple of his master, Nicolas of Cusa (1401–1464). The great Cardinal, in his *De Docta Ignorantia*, had propounded a general sceptical theory of human knowledge: finite intelligence is not able to assimilate precise truth and we must be content with an approximation; in particular, we can approach the essence of things, but we can never reach it. True Physics and Astronomy are inaccessible to man, they are known only to God. The only Physics attainable by us is one of fictions and abstractions.

Through the Cardinal's disciples, these ideas, with regard to astronomy in particular, made themselves strongly felt at Paris at the beginning of the 16th century.

Such theories as these emanating from the School of Paris are in marked contrast to the realism of the Italian philosophers of the same period. Whatever may be thought of the tendency towards metaphysical scepticism, the Parisians were on firm ground in the doctrine that the purpose of hypotheses, whether of the sub-lunary world or of the celestial world, is not to tell us of the nature of things, but simply to save the appearances.

This reasonable solution, in the line of Simplicius and St. Thomas, to end the interminable controversies, gradually lost ground however. The realist theory gained more and more adherents.

Copernicus in his *De Revolutionibus* (1543) is a simple realist. In his Dedicatory Preface to Paul III he refers to the lack of accord between the mathematicians (i.e. Averroists *v.* Ptolemaians). He believes that they have both failed, one party cannot explain all the phenomena, the other employs many inadmissible things. Consequently, Copernicus tells us, he sought for a system different to them both in which all the principles would be true and in accord with Nature, while at the same time yielding exact calculations of celestial phenomena.

However, the tradition of two orders was not yet forgotten. Curiously enough it is very clearly expounded in the Preface to Copernicus' own book, inserted anonymously by his editor, Osiander. 'It is not necessary that these hypotheses be true or even probable,' says Osiander; 'one thing alone suffices: that they afford calculations conforming to observation.' This is directly in the tradition of Simplicius and St. Thomas Aquinas.

Duhem has examined the opinions of a number of astronomers in the middle of the 16th century, both Protestant and Catholic. He finds fairly wide acceptance of the notion that the astronomer is concerned with fictions, and that in consequence the astronomer does not clash with the philosopher and theologian. *Hypotheses which flatly contradict the Scriptures, or which are in flagrant contradiction to sound philosophical principles, may yet be employed by the astronomer.*

But, as time goes on, the realist theory came more and more to hold sway: consequently we see a growing hostility of both theologians and philosophers to the Copernican hypotheses. Astronomy is put more and more in tutelage to metaphysics and theology.

Fr. Christopher Clavius, S.J., for instance, a leading astronomer in the latter part of the 16th century and Professor at the Roman College, examines the theory of two orders, but rejects it in favour of realism. On these principles he rejects the Copernican system as repugnant to both Philosophy and Scripture; it appears to him that the opinion of Ptolemy is to be preferred on both counts to that of Copernicus.[1]

The Protestant astronomer Tycho Brahe, at about the same time, held similar opinions. He regarded the dualism of Osiander as a mere subterfuge. For Tycho, as for Clavius, an astronomical hypothesis must not be false in Philosophy, nor must it be erroneous in Faith. He propounded a planetary

---

[1] Nevertheless the Gregorian reform of the Calendar in 1582, in which Clavius played a principal rôle, was accomplished by reference to Tables based on the Copernican system.

system of his own, lying between the systems of Ptolemy and Copernicus, and conforming to these requirements.

Another great astronomer, Johann Kepler, embraced the realist theory with enthusiasm; he utterly rejected the idea that astronomical hypotheses are merely convenient fictions. In the case of Kepler the system to be defended as representing the true nature of the world is Copernicanism.

Galileo likewise upheld realism; as with Kepler, it was directed towards the Copernican hypothesis. Galileo was convinced that the Copernican system was literally the one true structure of the heavens. He had nothing but scorn for the notion that these hypotheses were merely artifices. (Although, when occasion demanded it, he could pretend that he held this opinion).

The clash between the old and the new astronomical schools, both intransigeant realists, was mounting to greater and greater heights. The focus of controversy was the brilliant and witty person of Galileo. But there were still some, in all this Babel of tongues, who remembered the wise teaching that astronomical hypotheses were only mathematical devices, and that there was no need for all this bitter wrangling.

The wise and gentle Cardinal Bellarmine, S.J. (now Saint Robert Bellarmine), then chief theological adviser to the Holy See, tried to pour oil on troubled waters and avert the storm from Galileo's head, by appealing for recognition by Galileo of the fictional nature of all purely astronomical systems.[1] Cardinal Maffeo Barberini, later Pope Urban VIII, likewise entreated with Galileo that he should adopt a more prudent attitude towards the new astronomy; could not God produce the same effects by an indefinite number of different means? he asked. Why then *insist* on the scheme of Copernicus?

But realism won the day : and in the battle between the two schools of realists the Holy Office, as it must, lent its weight to the Ptolemaians. Galileo and the Copernicans were

---

[1] We have already alluded to this in Ch. XVII. Part of a letter of Bellarmine's on the subject is quoted on pp. 198-9.

censured, and their propositions condemned as false in Philosophy and erroneous in Faith.

In the course of time, by the irony of history, the process
was reversed. The realists had put astronomy under the
direction of philosophy and theology; as the prestige of
physical science grew, the pupil outstripped the master, and
philosophy and theology were popularly held in tutelage to
physics, still in the name of realism.

Since the time of Galileo, for a space of nearly three centuries,
we have traversed a passive interlude during which realism
has held undisputed sway, as we have related already (Ch. III).
The foundations were no longer critically examined; realism
was tacitly assumed everywhere. However, towards the end of
the 19th century critical enquiries were resumed; Ernst Mach
was one of the pioneers in this renaissance. Today realism still
commands popular thought; but the principle of two orders,
the real order and the artifact order, is gradually coming into
its own once more, and should in time drive out realism, and
so free philosophy and theology from this Babylonish captivity.

The dualist theory would seem to have the balance of
reason on its side. How then can we account for the tena-
cious hold of realism? Let us quote from two philosophers of
different periods who were quite familiar with the claims
of both schools of thought, but who yet chose realism.

The first is the Franciscan Friar, Bernard of Verdun, writing
in the 13th century. He expounds both sides in the clash
between the two astronomical systems of his day, and decides
in favour of the system of Ptolemy. He concludes, says
Duhem[1] 'that the hypotheses of this system are true, and that
truth is demonstrated by the accord which, for so long, is
maintained between their consequences and the observed
movements. We must consider them as truths of fact whose
certitude, immediately furnished by sensible experience,
escapes all the demonstration because it is anterior to it, and
commands it.' Referring to the Ptolemaic system Friar
Bernard writes 'up to now all its predictions are shown to be

[1] Duhem, *op. cit.*, pp. 291 f.

exact, and this would not be so if this point of departure were false; for, in all matters, a small error in the beginning becomes great at the end.'

We do not need to wait for John Stuart Mill for a clear exposition of physical realism.

Our second author is the Jesuit mathematician Christopher Clavius, writing at the end of the 16th century.[1] He expounds the opinion that astronomical hypotheses are designed to save the appearances. But, as previously remarked, he goes on to reject the notion. He writes: 'As one has not up to the present found a method more commodious than that which saves the appearances with the aid of eccentrics and epicycles, we are compelled to believe that the celestial spheres are constituted by orbs of this species.' To object that concordance with phenomena does not prove the reality of the hypothesis, would, Clavius thinks, destroy all physics, since this science is constructed entirely by rising from effects to causes.

It cannot be denied that these realist arguments, as they are stated by their exponents, have much weight. If the observer were simply a passive agent on whom is impressed the phenomena of the world, then we would have to grant a considerable truth to the realist doctrines. But, and here is the vital point, if we are not *passive* agents, but *active*, if we select and transform the phenomena of the world, and build up a highly artificial world of our own, if we impress our own laws upon the system of Nature, then the realist doctrine can no longer be sustained.

In physics and metaphysics we do *not* transform the world, we explore it as it is; in the mathematical astronomy of the ancients, and particularly of course in the exact mathematical science, mis-called physics, which has emerged since the days of Galileo, we select and transform and thereby pass away from the real world into the secondary world of mental artifacts.

[1] Duhem, *op. cit.*, pp. 561 f.

It was the failure to make allowances for our *activity* which turned people away from the doctrine of Simplicius and his successors to take up an intransigeant realism. In our own age we are only beginning to struggle free from the shackles of this doctrine.

# INDEX

Action, 34 n.
Action at a distance, 60 f.
Aesthetics, and positivism, 139 f.; and the artist, 155 n.
*Aeterni Patris*, Encyclical of Leo XIII, 201
Al Bitrogi, 236
Alexander the Great, 158
Algebra, 161 f.
*Almagest* of Ptolemy, 232, 236 f.
Alternating Current, theory of, 163
Analogy, 157
Analytic knowledge, 74 f.; and mathematical judgments, 84; and the philosophy of Wittgenstein, 99; and positivism, 139
Anatomist, and dissection, 5 f., 114
Animals, 120, 125
Anthropology, and the relativity of moral standards, 2
Antigone, 144
*a priori*, The, and laws of physics 25 f.; and the philosophy of Kant, 74 f., 164; origin of *a pr.* concepts, 83 f.; and Kant's dilemma, 87 f.; and philosophy of Wittgenstein, 97 f. and philosophy of C. I. Lewis, 101 f. ; and philosophy of Poincaré, 105 f.; and the philosophy of David Hume, 110 f.; and Kant's transcendental logic, 122 f.
Aquinas, St. Thomas, harmony of faith and reason, 3, 202, 227; on the Fall of Man, 9, 188; and Kant, 3–4, 94 f., 227; and law, 9 f., 165 n., 185; and the real sciences, 125, 156; and the social sciences, 169 f.; and universals, 181 f.; on astronomical theories, 195–6, 236; and the Leonine revival, 201; and hylomorphism, 211 f.; on God's existence, 214; on the sciences, 219 f.
Aristotelean science, 15 f., 156; Ar. science and observation, 19; Ar. doctrines and modern physics, 54 n., 57 n., 92 n., 199 f.; doctrine of matter and form, 64, 211 f.; Ar. science and the social sciences, 168 f.; Ar. sciences and history, 175; Ar. system and the 17th c. revolution, 193 ff., 203, 215 f.; Ar. science and General Relativity, 216
Aristotle, works of, 2; and Christian theology, 2; theory of science, 16, 125; *Physics*, 16 n., 231; and non-physical sciences, 45 f.; on atomism, 61; and the real sciences, 156; and political theory, 158; Ar.'s astronomy, 195, 232 f.; *De Caelo*, 195, 237; and Relativity, 197 n.; and hylomorphism, 211 f. ; Maimonides on Ar.'s astronomy, 235–6
Art, and the categorial, 12 n. ; and art critics, 121; and the real world, 131–2; schools of, 133; and positivism, 143; and Marxism, 149; and aesthetics, 155 n.
Artifacts, 35, 180-91, 228; and the categorial, 12, 121 f., 180 f.; and atoms, 64; and society, 121; in daily life, 131; and geometry, 160, 162 f.; and algebra, 161 f. ; and space, 161 f.; and number, 161 f.; and universals, 182 f.; their *raison d'être*, 185 f.; and the doctrine of *ens rationis*, 188 f.; and astronomy, 230 ff.
Astrology, 133
Astronomy, systems of, 41 n., 195 f., 232 ff.; method of, 152, 157–8; fictions in, 191; St. Thomas on theories in, 195–6, 237; and the Scriptures, 196 f., 239 f.; Bellarmine on, 198–9, 240 f.; ancient and medieval theories, 158 n., 230–43; Aristotle on, 232; Simplicius on, 233–4 ; Proclus on, 234–5; Maimonides on, 235–6; Averroes on, 236 f.; and the Humanists, 238; Nicholas of Cusa on, 238; Clavius on, 239 f.; Kepler on, 240; Galileo on, 240 f.; Urban VIII on, 240
Atom, Rutherford-Bohr model of, 62, 211–12, 216 f.; and theory of wave mechanics, 63; and hylomorphism, 211 f.

Blackwell
9-I-57